Dear

Many

- we hope you enjoyed
your trip.

With love
George, Jan, Sandra, Wendy,
Katie, Andrew and
George senior Imlach.

FORESTS, FIORDS & GLACIERS

The westerly scrapes
the core of the land
the blade of the mountain
spare Mt Cook, Rachel McAlpine

FORESTS, FIORDS
New Zealand's & *World Heritage*
GLACIERS

The Case for a
South-West New Zealand
World Heritage Site

Edited by
Gerard Hutching & Craig Potton

Royal Forest & Bird Protection Society of New Zealand
1987

Acknowledgements

The Society would like to thank all the contributors – both writers
and photographers – who have voluntarily provided material for
this book. We are particularly indebted to Craig Potton who has
collated most of the illustrations and Liz McMillan for her
patience in typing.

Cover:
Sea, sand, swamp and forest.
Ohinemaka Forest, South Westland.
Photo: Ray Joyce, Lansdowne Press

Back cover:
Kaka
Photo: P Daniel

Preliminary photos:
Fiordland crested penguin.
Photo: DoC

Mt Cook
Photo: Craig Potton

Kahikatea forest,
Waita River, South Westland.
Photo: Craig Potton

Milford area from
Gertrude Saddle, Fiordland.
Photo: Colin Monteath

Doubtful Sound, Fiordland.
Fear of adverse winds deterred
Captain Cook from entering this fiord
on his first voyage of discovery
in 1770.
Photo: Geoff Spearpoint

Published by
Royal Forest and Bird Protection
Society of New Zealand (Inc)
PO Box 631, Wellington,
New Zealand. (04) 728-154

ISBN 0 9597851 0 8

Designed by Margaret Cochran
Typeset by TypeHouse, Wellington
Printed and bound by Everbest Printing Co Ltd, Hong Kong

Contents

FOREWORD

THE PROSPECT of a South-West New Zealand World Heritage area is exciting to contemplate. Those of us who have praised the qualities of this corner of the world – that would include just about every New Zealander – believe that it rivals other natural southern temperate regions such as South America and south-west Tasmania. The latter is just one of the 63 premier natural areas in the world that have been created World Heritage sites to date.

No-one who has visited South-West New Zealand can fail to be touched by it. The overwhelming impression you are left with is the amazing diversity of the region. If measured in distance it would take the traveller the equivalent of from Hamilton to Wellington. Fortunately, there is no road stretching all the way from Okarito to Waitutu.

Thirty years ago I first travelled the dusty roads of Otago's interior towards an exciting world of complex and varied ecosystems – lowland to subalpine rainforests, wetlands, shrublands, alpine tussocklands, and high-alpine fellfields – all located in an impressive and dynamic landscape. My purpose was not just to admire this region but to try and understand it.

Over the years since then the South-West has figured in many conservation struggles.

In the early 1960s hundreds of us took part in the protracted battle to save Lakes Manapouri and Te Anau, threatened with desecration by an ill-conceived hydro-electric scheme. Today this dispute is seen as marking an important turning point in the ordinary New Zealander's concern for the environment.

When undertaking a vegetation survey of Mt Aspiring National Park over two summers in the late 1960s I was reassured to see the first signs of our palatable native plants recovering from the onslaught of deer browsing. Commercial hunters using helicopters were by then rapidly reducing their numbers. Since then there has been a spectacular resurgence of giant buttercups, ourisias, anisotomes and astelias, and the restoration of the alpine grasslands and herbfields to something of their former glory.

One of our notable endangered birds is the flightless takahe, which lives high up in the uncompromising environment of Fiordland's Murchison Mountains. There I have helped in studies aimed at saving this unique bird and have recently shared in the delight of improved prospects for the takahe, whose habitat has substantially recovered now that deer – competitors for critical items of the bird's diet – have been almost eliminated.

Further north, the battle to add South Okarito and Waikukupa lowland forests to Westland National Park was central to all of us involved in the conservation movement, and was finally won in 1981.

In September 1984 aboard a helicopter with David Bellamy and others I had the opportunity of viewing the ten marine terraces in Waitutu State Forest leading to the Hump Ridge. Impressed by the possible ecological significance of these unique terraces, I returned with 12 others the following autumn to conduct a comprehensive survey of them. The information we obtained should justify on scientific grounds the addition of Waitutu to Fiordland National Park.

Mt Aspiring (3072 m),
rises above the vast snowfields
of the Bonar Glacier,
Mt Aspiring National Park.
Photo: Lloyd Homer, Geological Survey, DSIR.

These are just a few of the areas of the South-West I have been fortunate enough to visit. Further areas being proposed for inclusion are Okarito Lagoon and the adjacent Waitangiroto Nature Reserve (white heron breeding area), the Olivine and Pyke State Forests, plus the areas of state forest in South Westland zoned for preservation once the Government decides on their future in 1988.

Along with many others I was disappointed that Mt Aspiring National Park was not declared a World Heritage Site in 1986 when Westland-Mt Cook and Fiordland National Parks were officially accepted. It seems that these three national parks were on an 'indicative list' for some time and were hastily promoted when the Government became a signatory to the World Heritage Convention soon after the general election in 1984. Clearly, Mt Aspiring is every bit as impressive and important as these other national parks.

Significantly, no private, Maori or Crown leasehold lands are involved in the World Heritage proposal. It is also important to dispel the notion that once World Heritage status is granted, New Zealand may lose its sovereign rights over the area and further, that only national parks can qualify as World Heritage sites. Nothing could be further from the truth. Indeed any area that has sufficiently high natural values and adequate formal protection can qualify. Moreover, New Zealand would continue to be in control of its own destiny in the South-West if World Heritage status was granted though its international reputation could suffer and the area could lose its enhanced status if the rules of the World Heritage Convention are flouted.

All of the areas being proposed are the responsibility of the new Department of Conservation, an aspect that should simplify their administration and official promotion of World Heritage status.

I believe, therefore, that few impediments should frustrate the proposal outlined and justified in this book for a South-West New Zealand World Heritage Area. I commend the

book to anyone with even a passing interest in natural history or nature conservation in New Zealand and especially the South Westland-Fiordland region. This book makes a convincing case for a South-West New Zealand World Heritage Area, both for the intrinsic value of the many natural ecosystems as well as for the increased reputation and economic benefit it will bestow on this country. And what better time to create it than during the 1987-88 centennial year of National Parks in New Zealand!

If you are convinced of the case I call on you to share it with others who may be less aware, particularly our politicians in whose hands the decision will ultimately rest.

Dr Alan Mark
President
Royal Forest & Bird Protection Society

Our Global Heritage

In Trust for Humankind

Gerry McSweeney

THE ISLANDS of Aotearoa are a remarkable biological treasure house. Many of our native plant and animal ancestors date from the great Gondwanaland supercontinent 80 million years ago, or have since arrived as hardy survivors of long-distance dispersal across the vast oceans that surround this land.

In the last 1000 years the arrival of people has brought phenomenal changes to the land and its inhabitants. Fire and forest clearance, hunting, the introduction of predators and of browsing mammals have transformed New Zealand. Today much of it resembles European pastureland or North American pine plantations while in places tatty remnants of shrubland begin the slow process of regeneration to native forest.

What is left today is certainly a shadow of its former glory but it is a heritage we increasingly recognise and appreciate and cannot afford to lose. World Heritage status provides an opportunity to recognise and protect the best areas that remain. In those parts of mainland New Zealand where rugged landscape has hindered settlement and where the climate is severe, soils are poor and the natural landscape remains least altered by human impact.

Inhospitable landscape

Pre-eminent amongst such areas is the South-West of the South Island. Contained within the South-West are classic examples of the evolutionary processes that have shaped the earth. The great Alpine Fault divides the region and is the junction of the Indian and Pacific continental plates. Collision between these plates is thrusting up the Southern Alps which rise to nearly 4,000 m altitude from sea level in a mere 30 km. Vast natural erosion processes equal the mountain uplift of 12 mm annually. This erosion chokes rivers with debris and is actively building up the coastal lowlands.

Glaciers which still mantle much of the South Westland mountain landscape accelerate the erosion of the region's mountains. In earlier times far more extensive glaciers, the largest in Australasia, carved the fiords and blanketed the South Westland coastal plain to the sea. The beech and podocarp swamp forests that have since spread across this landscape have survived because of New Zealand's isolation from more advanced evolutionary forces in the northern hemisphere and most closely resemble the ancient forests of Gondwanaland. These forests are inhabited by distinctive native animals although these have suffered from the impact of human settlement and the liberation of predators. Good populations of uncommon birds like the kaka, blue duck, yellowhead, Fiordland crested penguin and two species of kiwi are still widespread. Also present are rare species such as the majestic takahe, the kakapo, a range of swamp dwelling native fish and native bats.

The South-West was the point of first contact for the great European navigators. However, sheer-walled fiords, brawling flood-prone rivers, wet infertile lowlands, hordes of biting sandflies and a climate, particularly in spring and autumn, notorious for a succession of westerly storms have repulsed all but the hardiest European settlers. By contrast there is considerable archaeological evidence recently discovered to suggest that

Far left:
Tall red beech forest, Dart Valley. Red beech grows on the richest soils of the lower slopes and valley floors, particularly in the upper Arawata-Hollyford valleys in the west and Dart-Eglinton valleys in the east. Red beech distribution is limited in the South-West by a combination of cold climate, poor soils and past effects of glaciation.
Photo: Geoff Spearpoint

Overleaf:
From a glacier-fed lake beneath the northern face of Mt Aspiring, the Waiatoto River flows 33 km down a mountain valley then meanders across the forested Haast lowlands to the Tasman Sea. Walls of rimu and kahikatea forest line its lower reaches. Tributaries flow into the Waiatoto from extensive open swamps, making this river very important for whitebait.
Photo: Ian Platt, DoC

15

Maori were scattered along the Haast to Milford coastline in considerable numbers for nearly a millenium until European settlement. Significantly a number of the few settlers found in the area today have also developed a hunter-gatherer lifestyle. Hunting, fishing and low-impact lifestyles are a distinctive cultural feature of the South-West worthy of equal recognition with the natural values.

With such an inhospitable landscape for European settlement it comes then as no surprise that successive New Zealand governments conformed to the worldwide tradition of preserving only those areas with little human economic use for farming or forestry. It is estimated that only one half of one percent of New Zealand's land area has been designated a national park or reserve where this land also had potential for production (Molloy and Enting 1981). Fiordland National Park was created in 1905, Westland National Park in 1960, Mt Aspiring soon after in 1964 and, more recently the Hooker Landsborough Wilderness Area has just been approved. Most montane and alpine parts of South-West New Zealand are therefore already legally protected.

In the lowlands of the South West, however, it is a different story. From the great Waitutu forest in the South, through the Cascade and Pyke river lowlands west of Mt Aspiring, north across the kahikatea forest and swamps of the Haast-Paringa region to Westland National Park, lowland native forests have been excluded from legal protection. Despite their intractable soils, hostile farming climate and isolation, these areas have been, and by some still are, considered ripe for exploitation.

Now after devastating virtually all the remaining lowland forest elsewhere in New Zealand, the timber industry has come to assault New Zealand's largest remaining wilderness. A recent timber industry paper on the region estimated that southern Westland contained 5.7 million cubic metres of predominantly rimu and kahikatea timber. It advocated the 'sustained yield management' (sic) of this resource despite abundant evidence further north of such logging techniques being both an economic and environmental disaster.

The Forests, Fiords and Glaciers World Heritage story then is a familiar one worldwide. New Zealand's last area to escape humans' 'civilising' influence is now the next in line. Logging, mining, tourist roading and agricultural expansion all offer the same end result – wilderness diminished. The same unpalatable choices are simultaneously being offered to Indonesian and Amazon rainforests, to the vast herds of the East African savannah and to the natural communities of the Antarctic.

World Heritage Convention

There is, however, one bright prospect that unifies the world's threatened habitats in a concept that is as grand as it is compelling. Just imagine the legendary wonders of the world recognised and elevated to international status as the common heritage of all mankind. The focus of world attention, such areas would also be the focus of world efforts to encourage respective governments to protect such areas and where necessary other nations will economically assist them to do so. This is the World Heritage Convention in action.

In the second half of the twentieth century it has become all too apparent that vital parts of the world's natural and cultural heritage are being lost. It is a legacy of the blind rush to 'develop' resources and consequent poor planning, poor management and the lack of commitment to conservation.

By 1972, widespread awareness of this problem culminated at an international level in three environmental programmes. UNESCO began its Man and the Biosphere programme, the United Nations Environment programme was launched in Stockholm and the 2nd International Conference on National Parks was held in Grand Teton, USA.

The World Heritage concept arose from these discussions and finally in November 1972 the 'Convention for the Protection of the World Cultural and Natural Heritage' – the World Heritage convention – was adopted by the General Conference. It was to provide a framework for international co-operation in conserving the world's outstanding natural and cultural properties.

What do the Pyramids of Egypt, the Grand Canyon of Colorado and Australia's Great Barrier Reef have in common? Or the Taj Mahal, Machu Picchu of the ancient Inca in the Andes and Australia's Kakadu National Park? In one sense very little, except they are all monuments or places of natural splendour. Were they ever to disappear it would represent an irreplaceable loss for each and everyone of us.

Today these monuments and places are recorded together with many others on the same list, the World Cultural and Natural Heritage List. The ancient Greeks identified 'Seven Wonders of the World' which they then knew. Today practically all have disappeared.

There is a lesson in today's world where far more than seven wonders are recognised. Our test is to preserve the most significant testimonies of past civilisations, and of our present cultures as well as the world's outstanding natural areas.

By adopting the World Heritage Convention, nations recognise that each country holds in trust for the rest of mankind those parts of the world's heritage – both natural and cultural – that are found within its boundaries; that the international community has an obligation to support any nation in meeting this trust, if its own resources are insufficient; and that mankind must exercise the same sense of responsibility to the works of nature as to the works of its own hands. However, sovereignty of any World Heritage site remains with the country where the site is located.

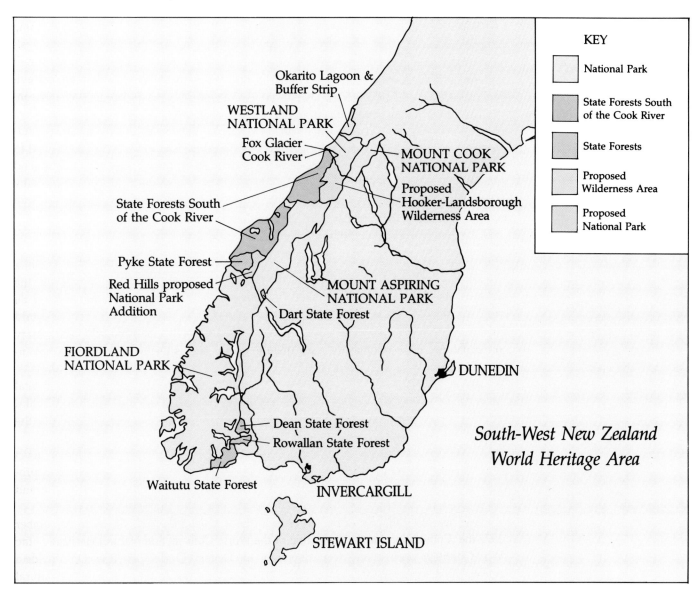

KEY

National Park

State Forests South of the Cook River

State Forests

Proposed Wilderness Area

Proposed National Park

South-West New Zealand World Heritage Area

By 1985, 85 countries had adopted the Convention and nearly 200 World Heritage sites had been recognised in more than 50 countries.

Under the Convention, a committee of member governments is established to decide which areas are to be accepted as World Heritage sites. It also decides which threatened World Heritage sites are given special recognition on the World Heritage in Danger List (which can lead to emergency assistance). The committee also advises on the allocation of the World Heritage Fund which is used to provide technical and financial assistance to protect World Heritage sites. The Fund originates from a levy on all countries that are signatories to the World Heritage Convention and from voluntary contributions. In Nepal's Sagarmatha (Mt Everest) National Park, for example, the Fund is supporting solar power development to reduce demands on scarce firewood and so save surrounding forests. In Tanzania, it is helping fund the College of Wildlife Management which trains staff from the country's World Heritage Parks such as Serengeti and the Ngorongoro Crater.

The World Heritage Convention is unique because it deals with both cultural and natural properties. Certain archaeological sites or ancient buildings have an impact on history, art or science that transcends geographical boundaries; some townsites or groups of buildings are of special significance because of their architecture or place in the landscape; and some sites bear exceptional witness to a civilisation which has since disappeared.

These outstanding works of man are an irreplaceable part of the world's cultural heritage. The majority of World Heritage sites, nearly 150 in total, are recognised as cultural properties. They include sites which reveal humans evolving with their environment as well as some of the best known or infamous constructions of the world's past and contemporary civilisations such as Chartres Cathedral, Auschwitz concentration camp, Versailles Palace and Jerusalem.

The Lower Valley of the Awash in Ethiopia has revealed the most complete skeleton of early pre-man yet known, and a whole family of early humans has been found, providing the earliest evidence of human social behaviour. From a nearby site on the Omo River come the earliest indications of human industry, in the form of stone tools. The use of tools gave people their dominant position in the animal kingdom.

At the Willandra Lakes site in Australia is recorded some of the earliest evidence of harvesting fresh-water animals and using grindstones to crush wild grass seeds to flour, showing man's evolving ability to harvest nature's goods.

World Heritage Criteria

Our natural heritage is an equally priceless legacy. A natural property proposed for the List must meet at least one of the following four criteria (though meeting more than one criterion does not necessarily imply a more valuable site):

1   *be an outstanding example representing the major stages of the earth's evolutionary history (for example, fossil beds, geological sites, ice-age landscapes);*

2   *be an outstanding example representing significant ongoing geological processes, biological evolution, and human interaction with the natural environment (for example, volcanoes, tropical rainforests, terraced agricultural landscapes);*

3   *contain superlative natural phenomena, formations, or features, or areas of exceptional natural beauty (for example, superlative mountains or waterfalls, great concentrations of animals);*

4   *contain the foremost natural habitats where threatened species of animals or plants of outstanding universal value can survive.*

Significantly just over a quarter of the 200 World Heritage sites are natural properties. This indicates an imbalance towards cultural properties which urgently needs to be corrected. For example, despite the enormous ecological significance of tropical rain-forests and their severely threatened status, the tropical rainforests of the Amazon basin and South-East Asia have not yet been included on the World Heritage Lists. Nevertheless, the World Heritage List of natural properties is most impressive.

The Grand Canyon shows the physical conflict between mountain building and natural erosion in a geological record covering two thousand million years. Yellowstone has the world's largest concentration of hot springs and geysers illustrating the active evolution of the earth's crust. Ecuador's Galapagos Islands which originate from volcanic eruptions at sea, provide a perfect laboratory for the study of evolution, inspiring Charles Darwin and many others since him.

The culmination of the evolutionary process can be seen at Virunga National Park in Zaire. Ranging from equatorial forest to mountain glaciers, the site may have the greatest diversity of habitats in the world, as well as some of the most interesting plants and animals.

Many World Heritage sites are of critical importance in conserving major concentrations of wildlife. The great herds of plain animals and their predators in Tanzania's Serengeti National Park provide one of the most remarkable and inspiring wildlife spectacles in the world.

The world's longest coral reef is also a World Heritage site. Composed of a long series of reefs and islands separated by navigable channels, Australia's Great Barrier Reef is being built by over 400 species of corals, providing a habitat for a host of marine animals.

Quartz boulders carried down from southern Fiordland's mountains by glaciers and rivers line the wild south coast of the Waitutu forest.
Photo: Les Molloy

In the wild South-West, nature reigns supreme. A day's nor-west rain can turn even gentle streams into raging torrents, such as this flooded waterfall in the Dart River catchment.
Photo: Geoff Spearpoint

Roaring Forties wilderness

The southern wilderness landscape of the roaring forties with their vegetation and land-form links dating back to the great southern continent of Gondwanaland have already been partly recognised and protected. Argentina's Los Glaciares National Park is a maze of lakes, glaciers and beech forest which bears a striking resemblance to many parts of New Zealand and to Tasmania. The Western Tasmania Wilderness National Parks were accepted for World Heritage listing as both a natural and cultural property in December 1982. Threats to this led to Australia's Federal Government intervening in 1983 to prevent the construction of the Franklin Dam. This would have flooded the magnificent rainforested Franklin Valley and destroyed the Kutakina cave system which preserves the earliest record of aboriginal occupation of Tasmania, 21,000 years ago.

> *The primary objective of a World Heritage Site is to protect the natural features on the basis of which the area was considered to be of World Heritage quality. This is normally accomplished through existing national legislation and most World Heritage Sites will already have National Park or strict Nature Reserve status. In some cases, reserved forest area may be considered but only when they are assured of perpetual protection.*   IUCN 1982

World Heritage status can encompass a range of lands of different protective tenures, provided their protection is permanent. World Heritage status also recognises that cultural elements are a vital component of natural ecosystems.

Traditional lifestyles are recognised and safeguarded for people such as the Masai who live within the East African wildlife areas and the rainforest inhabitants of Zaire's Virunga National Park. Although it is accepted that many areas of international importance have already been protected without World Heritage status, by having areas recognised as World Heritage sites, nations can then also receive the collective recognition and co-operation of other nations in protecting the heritage of all mankind.

Conferring of World Heritage status does not allow outside nations or the World Heritage Committee to infringe upon a nation's sovereignty in seeking protection for an area. Article 6 of the Convention specifically refers to it 'fully respecting the sovereignty of the states of whose territory' areas etc. are situated and also respects 'property rights provided by national legislation.'

The only powers the Convention bestows on the international community are those of persuasion, encouragement and the offering of technical or financial incentives to safeguard threatened Heritage areas. If these fail, the only power remaining to the World Heritage Committee is to remove World Heritage status from a threatened site with consequent damage to a nation's international image.

The classification of World Heritage carries with it great international prestige. The World Heritage committee publishes a list of these areas of 'outstanding universal value' and this promotion together with publicity material produced by countries about their own sites results in increased tourism. For example in the United States the Mesa Verde National Park with its deserted cave dwellings was recognised as a World Heritage site in 1978. Within four years the number of international visitors to the park increased from 6 per cent of all visitors to 30 per cent. Just across the Tasman Sea the Tasmanian Tourist Bureau is placing heavy emphasis on their Western Wilderness World Heritage in a bid to lure mainland Australian and New Zealand visitors.

New Zealand became a state party to the World Heritage Convention on the 22 November 1984 and became eligible to nominate areas as World Heritage sites. The obvious candidates to seize upon were our existing National Parks. In an unimaginative approach the New Zealand Government nominated Mt Cook/Westland (our highest mountains) and Fiordland (our largest) National Parks as World Heritage Sites in late 1985. Their acceptance by the World Heritage Committee was announced by the New Zealand Government in November 1986.

Lakes Manapouri and Te Anau (shown here) were carved out by Fiordland's glaciers in the Ice Ages. Both lakes are a powerful symbol to the conservation movement of the ability of ordinary people to prevent despoilation of New Zealand's scenic gems. Island-studded Manapouri, within Fiordland National Park, was threatened by a power scheme which would have raised the lake, drowning islands and the natural shoreline. The subsequent nation-wide protest campaign powerfully influenced the 1972 general election and succeeded in the passage of a law which preserves the lakes' levels within their natural range.
Photo: Eric Taylor

Woodchipping is already devastating Rowallan forest at the southern fringe of the proposed World Heritage area, feeding Japan's insatiable appetite for the world's hardwood rainforests.
Photo: Gerry McSweeney

Wilderness continues to be eroded on a worldwide basis at an alarming rate. In the South-West, destructive logging has already made significant incursions, such as here at Waiho Beach near the river outlet of the Franz Josef Glacier where dense kahikatea swamp forest has been clearfelled since the 1970s. With the creation of a South-West World Heritage area, there still remains the possibility to protect most of the remaining kahikatea forest from the ravages of logging.
Photo: Gerry McSweeney

Right:
The shrill, ringing notes from flocks of yellowheads used to fill South Island forests with birdsong. Today, however, the yellowhead has disappeared from most of its former range, with South-West New Zealand its final stronghold. Vital to this attractive bird's continued survival are extensive stands of mature red and silver beech trees, for it is in these that the yellowhead makes its home. The Landsborough, Dart and Eglinton Valleys, and Western Southland beech forests provide the best habitat for this bird.

Inset:
Scientists are attempting to find out why the yellowhead has become so threatened.
Photos: Don Hadden

In a 19 January 1987 editorial titled 'Our World Heritage', Wellington's *Dominion* newspaper welcomed the inclusion of the three parks on the World Heritage List. However, it also gave some insights into the grander opportunities the World Heritage Convention could offer New Zealand.

> *The inclusion of Fiordland and Mt Cook/Westland National Parks into the World Heritage Sites designated by UNESCO is a welcome reminder of the riches New Zealanders have on their doorstep. Too often in our history lipservice has been paid to our unique environment while at the same time land has been laid needlessly to waste. Hopefully the designation of World Heritage Sites will contribute to an era of wiser husbandry.*
>
> *The areas thus far included amount to a cautious approach in the sense that they are already protected to the highest degree possible under New Zealand statutes. Logically other surrounding areas should eventually be incorporated into the sites...*
>
> *Already within the sites, Mt Cook and Milford Sound are suffering from intense tourism pressure. Rather than increase that, the World Heritage status should be used to spread the benefits more widely. A decision to do this has some quite specific impacts. The most immediate involves the decision over the future of the kahikatea forests south of the Westland National Park. The forests are state owned, but unprotected by National Park or World Heritage status. The Government is committed to a decision by June 30 this year. At present a logging moratorium is in effect and with no mill or existing jobs directly affected the sensible option appears to be to use the tourism potential of the forests and include them in a World Heritage Site.*

New Zealand is at a crossroads. We can proceed in a haphazard and piecemeal approach to assess, protect and manage each of the many individual parcels of public natural land in the South-West – places like the Red Hills, Waitutu, the kahikatea forests, the freshwater wetlands, and of course the National Parks. Each will be managed in its individual, and often inconsistent and incompatible way. There will be good management, there will be bad management but above all the opportunity will be lost to recognise the unity of the wild South-West.

Alternatively we can seize the opportunity the World Heritage concept presents of integrated recognition, protection and promotion.

In 1987-1988, New Zealand celebrates its centennial of National Parks. Soon after we celebrate 150 years as a nation.

To embrace the South-West New Zealand World Heritage concept is to provide a legacy that every New Zealander and people throughout the world can cherish and protect.

Far left:
The sustained rain and snow of the Roaring Forties gives rise to extensive glaciers along the Southern Alps. Here the Volta (top) and Therma glaciers of Mt Aspiring National Park join to form the Waiatoto River.
Photo: Geoff Spearpoint

Overleaf:
Sea to mountains across Waikukupa forest, now part of Westland National Park. Waikukupa and South Okarito forests stand as symbols of the struggle to protect lowland forests. From 1975 thousands of people campaigned for these to be added to the park.
Their efforts were rewarded in 1982, protecting for all time an expanse of natural land from the Tasman Sea to the highest peaks of the Southern Alps. Mt Tasman (left), Mt Cook (right).
Photo: Craig Potton

CHAPTER TWO

Geology, Glaciation & Landforms

A Rugged and Dynamic Landscape

Craig Potton

New Zealand is an old land with a young landscape –
a paradox that is nowhere truer than in South Westland. Peter Wardle, botanist

SOME ROCKS of the south-western corner of New Zealand are very old, but all the landforms are exceedingly young. It is a restless land whose mountains are not only perceptibly rising against a severe rate of erosion, but are also being slowly rent apart along a gargantuan faultline. Such has been the price of standing astride two of the earth's largest and most active crustal plates.

Just yesterday in geological time huge glaciers carved out U-shaped valleys depositing massive moraine heaps all the way to the ocean. And while spectacular glaciers continue to grind away at the mountains today so does a rainfall which can exceed 14,000 mm a year and turn rivers into seething torrents. South-West New Zealand is simply one of the most dynamic landscapes in the world which is not presided over by active volcanoes.

Gondwanaland

For most of its geological history, New Zealand has been a coastal fringe and dumping ground for eroded sediments and volcanic debris from a huge southern continent called Gondwanaland. This supercontinent included lands we now call Antarctica, Australia, South America, India and Africa. The importance of the Gondwanaland connection and New Zealand's timely severance from it is described in later chapters on New Zealand's ancient flora and fauna.

The geological turbulence of the region is directly attributable to the meeting of two massive earth plates in this arena which New Zealand has occupied for at least the last 500 million years. According to the theory of 'plate tectonics', vast sections of the earth's crust are rafted over the surface by convection currents in the underlying mantle. New mantle material is pushed up on to the surface from deep ocean trenches causing sea floors and accompanying lighter continental rocks to spread out until they meet another crustal plate. Volcanoes, mountain chain uplift, massive folding, faulting and metamorphism, surface out-crops of deep mantle rocks, earthquakes – these are all continuing features of New Zealand's geological evolution which indicate the country's collision position between the Pacific and Indo-Australian plates.

Fiordland is the largest block of New Zealand's most ancient rocks (other outcrops all occur west of the Alpine Fault in Westland and North-West Nelson). Fossils of graptolites – floating colonies of small marine animals – date rocks of southern Fiordland to at least 500 million years ago. Eroded from an ancient Gondwanaland complex, these fossil-bearing sediments have avoided the intense metamorphism common to most of the region. The complex matrix of Fiordland includes igneous basalts and andesites, plutonic

The mountain upthrust of the Southern Alps reaches its apex in the Westland/Mt Cook National Park region. Mt Tasman, 3498 m, (foreground) is regarded as New Zealand's finest ice peak. Huge icefields of the Fox, Franz Josef and Tasman (right) glaciers radiate east and west of the Main Divide.

Photo: Lloyd Homer, Geological Survey, DSIR.

igneous rocks such as diorite, gabbro and granite, a whole host of metamorphic rocks like schist and sedimentary sandstones, conglomerates and limestone (occurring down the eastern and southern fringes).

The most ancient parts of Fiordland were uplifted during a mountain building period known as the Tuhua Orogeny 395-345 million years ago during which intense deformation and metamorphism occurred. About 280-225 million years ago a line of volcanic eruptions occurred off the coast to the east of the older metamorphic rocks. This volcanic activity seems to have marked the subduction zone between the crustal plates which has continued to play such a dominant role in New Zealand's geology since.

This volcanic activity took place in a sea basin wedged between the coasts of eastern Australia and Antarctica. For the next 150 million years it was a vast collecting ground for sand and silt eroded from these continents. Layers of sediments were gradually compressed into hard sandstones and siltstones (greywacke and argillite) creating most of the rocks in the region. Intense pressure at the bottom of the trough metamorphosed these rocks into the schists now seen on the western side of the Southern Alps.

140 to 120 million years ago this underwater deposition was suddenly subjected to a major collision of continental masses on the two adjacent plates and thrust up as an ancestral New Zealand landmass. Nearly all the rocks which now form the backbone of South-West New Zealand were uplifted then but they were far from their present place. This mountainous landmass was eroded away over the next 100 million years to a few hummocky hills above the lapping waves. Equally significantly a massive skewing of the earth's crust was to displace these formations down an impressive faultline.

Alpine Fault

The South Island's Alpine Fault is said to be one of few faults in the world visible from space. Over 600 km long and extending in a virtually straight line on the western edge of the Southern Alps, from Milford Sound to the Spenser Mountains in Nelson, the fault dramatically marks the point where the Indo-Australian plate crashes into its Pacific counterpart. Over at least the last 30 million years the fault has ripped apart rocks which once laid side by side moving them a distance of 450 km. Ultramafic rocks of the 'red hills' in Otago on the eastern side of the fault are precisely matched by 'red hills' behind Nelson, on the western side of the fault. In similar patterns the granites of Fiordland and the schists of Otago are matched by the granites of North-West Nelson and the schists of Marlborough. The fault is very visible by aeroplane, especially where it marks the steep western scarp of the Southern Alps and captures rivers like the Jackson and Cascade, causing them to run parallel to the coast for a considerable distance.

Captain Cook came to the Pacific searching for a great southern continent that was supposed to balance the landmass of Europe and Asia in the northern hemisphere, but Gondwanaland had already broken up 60 million years beforehand. Furthermore, if Abel Tasman, the first European explorer to see New Zealand, arrived a mere 10 million years earlier he would not have seen his 'land uplifted high'. New Zealand's third mountain building phase has only shown its startling results within the last 10 million years and continues unabated today.

In the last three million years the uplift of the central alps around Mt Cook has

The collision of two of the earth's largest crustal plates has created the ruler straight line of the Alpine Fault, clearly visible in this satellite photo over South Westland. The light red is farmland, the dark brown native forest.

equalled 18,000 m – over five times the height of Mt Cook. In fact the uplift is occurring at such a rate that despite the massive erosion in the alps, the mountains rise from the western coastal plains at awe inspiring angles. In a mere 30 km from the ocean the peaks climb to 3500 m, forming the highest and most spectacular mountains in Australasia.

Glaciation

While the erosion of ancient land masses, volcanoes and intrusive material formed the rock types, and the crushing of crustal plates has caused the great mountain chain of the Southern Alps to rise, the main force which has shaped the present landscape has been glacial ice. South-West New Zealand is a World Heritage show case of past and present glacial processes. Here the power of the last two million years of the Ice Ages is graphically rendered in the shapes of the valleys and mountains and faintly echoed in the present glaciers.

In a series of advances and retreats over the past two million years, ice has gathered in the high névé basins of the alps to begin its remorseless path to the sea. From the highest peaks to beyond the coast the cold hand of ice has sculptured massive forms: alpine basins and cirques, sharp arête peaks and ridges, prominent rounded monoliths of hard resistant rock, entrapped lakes, linear and arching moraines enveloped in forests, impounded lagoons and a host of other formations. At the height of the ice advances the major valleys were over 1000 m deep in ice and much of the lowland region was covered in a thinner sheet of piedmont ice until the present valley systems emerged across the lowland. Most of the soil, plants and animals were swept away before the advances although some notable pockets of lee slopes and plateaux provided valuable refuges for the hardier species. As a consequence of these advances few surfaces of South Westland are older than 20,000 years.

Although the whole region displays the unmistakeable scars of invasions by ice, three areas – the central alps, Fiordland and the Westland coastal plains and hills – are quite remarkable examples of different features caused by the power of moving bodies of frozen water.

Fiordland is a showcase of the rasping power of the gravels and boulders trapped in the ice and attacking the resistant walls of a very tough parent rock. The huge glaciers and hard rocks have produced some of the most impressive U-shaped valleys in the world, creating the 2000 m sea cliffs of the fiords as sea levels rose after the last glaciation. A multitude of alpine lakes nestled high in cirque basins have outlets which suddenly plunge into space as awesome waterfalls where side valleys join the main valleys.

Whereas the story of Fiordland's ice sculpting is as an echo of past events, in the central alps the same processes are very much active today. The extensive, high névé fields of the Fox and Franz Josef glaciers pressure their ice outlets down through narrow steep gorges to reach carparks a mere 300 m above sea level. Here the glaciers move at a rapid 2-3 m per day compared to the 18-km long Tasman Glacier which lumbers along at a more sedate 65 cm per day.

The western coastal plains and hills are largely composed of billions of tonnes of rubble eroded from the Southern Alps by glacial action and deposited either during the ice advance as walls of lateral or terminal moraine or after the ice retreated by erosion from the glaciated mountains. These walls of moraine have been sculptured into curving patterns by the moving ice and further softened in outline by the forest mantle. In South Westland the full sequence of glacial action from the mountains to the sea remains in a state largely unmodified by people but prey to the phenomenal forces of erosion in this dynamic landscape where the rainfall exceeds 10,000 mm in the outer ranges.

Since the ice has retreated, a lush plant cover has partially stabilised the land but with the removal of the pressure of the ice on steep faces in the alps and the immense rainfall the rate of erosion remains at a colossal level. River valleys in the troughs carved by the great glaciers during the final extension have subsequently filled with gravel silt and peat, with the exception of numerous lowland lakes.

Coastal landscape

The westerly wind-driven sea also has contributed immensely to the coastal landscape, creating long sweeping curves of sand and gravel embayments and spits between promontories where bold sea cliffs have been carved from the ancient lateral moraines. The great coastal plain around Haast has an unusual origin. Here, over the last 6-8,000 years, a series of sand dunes have been built up by the action of the sea. These parallel dune ridges extend for several kilometres inland and are forest-covered. Between some of the dunes there are long, narrow lagoons and inland from the dunes are large lagoons representing embayments from what was once part of the sea. The swampy, coastal plain is being slowly transformed into dry land by stream-borne deposits from the surrounding hills, infilling these embayments.

Criteria for World Heritage status include 'outstanding examples of the earth's evolutionary history' and 'geological processes'. In meeting these criteria South-West New Zealand displays: a substantial portion of the massive Alpine Fault (junction of the Pacific and Indo-Australian Plates), the most startling examples of contemporary mountain building in Australasia, the finest examples of Australasian pleistocene glaciation (past and present) and one of the earth's most active non-volcanic environments where uplift and erosion, soil formation and degradation are all played out in an exaggerated fashion.

Land uplifted high. The Southern Alps are rising at about the same rate as they are being eroded away – approximately 15-20 mm a year. Mt Elie de Beaumont (3109 m), Mt Cook National Park.
Photo: Gerard Hutching

Soils of the South-West

Gerry McSweeney

The forest soils of the South-West are among the poorest in the world. At Okarito downward leaching to an impervious pan at a metre depth has left this white layer in the rooting zone virtually devoid of soil nutrients. When the forest cover in such areas is removed, it also takes away most of the nutrients, leaving impoverished soils unlikely to grow another tall forest.
Photo: Les Molloy

FOR MANY of us the most important thing about soils is how well they grow cabbages in our backyard. In most of urban and farmed areas of New Zealand cabbage growing is fairly straightforward.

However, were we to try growing cabbages over most of the South-West we would be very disappointed by the result – almost everywhere the soils are too wet, cold or old. The German settlers dumped in the South-West in the late 1800s at Jamestown, Lake McKerrow and at Jacksons Bay discovered this the hard way. The lushness of the rainforests belied the impoverished soils on which they grew. Dreams of food self-sufficiency gave way to desperate reality and the settlements were abandoned by the early 1900s.

Maori inhabitants of the South-West prior to the failed German settlers had long realised that the bounty of the region lay not in its soils and horticulture but in the harvest of birds from its forests and fish from the waters. Their hunter-gatherer lifestyle was well suited to the region.

The development of soils is a function of many factors – the forest vegetation, the parent rock, soil organisms, the climate and time. Over most of the South-West, climate and time are the dominant influences. The whole region is subject to sustained heavy rainfall. As a consequence on any freshly exposed rock surfaces soils form quickly. They also leach and age quickly. This cycle is classically illustrated in soils found on the moraines of the Franz Josef glacier. These moraines have been deposited in successive small advances across the coastal plain since the glaciers retreated from the seacoast after the last great Ice Age 20,000 years ago. The Franz Josef age sequence of soils has been intensively studied and is internationally regarded as one of the world's finest examples of the formation and ageing of soils.

On the youngest glacial moraines – some 20 years old – nitrogen fixing shrubs, grasses and herbs are building up soils. By 150 years of age 20-metre high rata-kamahi forests will be growing on a deep black soil which now blankets the moraines.

By 3,000 years tall rimu forest dominates the moraines. However, heavy rainfall is now progressively leaching nutrients downwards in the soil so they are unavailable to plants. On 20,000 year and older soils the tall rimu forests become steadily more stunted giving way to silver pine, bog pine and even low heathland and red tussock. These plants are adapted to the extreme infertility and acidity of the old leached moraine soils. The old soils can no longer support tall forest (nor even cabbages!) until the next advance of the glacier across the coastal plain blankets the landscape in fresh moraine debris to begin the soil cycle once again.

This pattern is repeated throughout the South-West. The soils of the old moraines, older terraces and dunes and of the flatter hillsides are generally leached and infertile. Mountain beech, rimu and silver pine dominate such sites. In river valleys often rejuvenated by frequent floods, the soils are younger and comparatively fertile. Tall nutrient-demanding kahikatea, totara, silver and red beech forests characterise such areas. In many places these forests have already been cleared for farming.

Steeper hillsides are subject to constant downslope flushing of soil nutrients. Slips and landslides also constantly expose fresh sites to soil development. Consequently the steepland soils of the mountain slopes are of medium fertility and support red and silver beech and nutrient-demanding hardwoods such as ribbonwood, wineberry, pigeonwood and mahoe.

Higher up the mountainsides the rainfall increases and the temperature decreases. Soils develop much more slowly and leaching is even faster. On flatter sites where soils have time to develop without being eroded, this severe cold, wet climate, especially characteristic on the low-nutrient granite and gneiss rock of Fiordland, leads to the

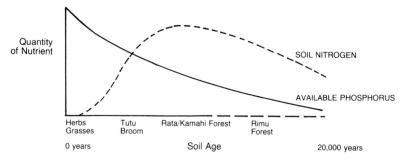

Nitrogen (N) and phosphorus (P) are two key nutrients for plant growth. The diagram shows that over a period of time the pattern of soil formation on glacial moraines shows a steady increase in nitrogen levels in the early stages, but a decrease in the available phosphorus.

development of blanket peats that closely resemble the peat moorlands of Britain and the Arctic tundra.

Of course there are exceptions to these general patterns; none more so than soils on the mineral-rich rock of the Red Hills. So high are the chromium and magnesium levels in these soils that they inhibit plant growth. This results in the stunted vegetation that dominates the Cascade and Gorge Plateaux, much of the Red Hills and hillsides near Anita Bay further south in Fiordland. Fairly low nutrient soils develop on the sedimentary greywackes of Mt Cook and the gneiss and granite of Fiordland. However, the schist rocks in the valleys of Mt Aspiring where rainfall is lower than further west, break down easily and develop comparatively fertile soils. This is reflected in the lush growth of clover grasses in some of these mountain valleys and the magnificent red and silver beech forests in areas such as the lower Dart valley.

Overall however, there is one clear message to humankind from the soils of the South-West. Perhaps we could call it the 'lesson of the cabbages'. Here lies a concentration of some of the poorest soils in the world interspersed by pockets of medium to poor river valley and hill slope soils. Undisturbed, it will continue to support a magnificent array of vegetation types, each of which illustrates the golden rule that nature abhors a vacuum and that plants have adapted to cope with the conditions of that site.

We disturb such areas at our peril. They are infertile, they are severely erosion-prone and they are flood-prone. For forestry and agriculture they are the least attractive sites in New Zealand. That is why they remain in their natural state to the present day.

Remove the forests and one removes the soils' protective blanket against storms. One also removes the vegetation which contains most of the ecosystem's available nutrients. Rather than storing nutrients in the soil, where they would be subject to intense leaching, the South-West rainforests – like those of the Amazon – store most of their nutrients above ground in trunks, leaves and twigs. Remove these and you not only destroy the present forest but also forest in the future.

Ice caves form in deeply crevassed
sections of the major glaciers.
Photo: Craig Potton

Far left:
In Fiordland, temperate rainforest
defies gravity and mountain torrents.
Photo: Craig Potton

Overleaf:
The immense geological forces
at play in the South-West are
graphically demonstrated in the Red
Hills range of West Otago. These
remarkable iron and magnesium-rich
rocks were thrust into position by a
collision of the earth's plates hundreds
of millions of years ago. Since then the
Alpine Fault has wrenched the range
apart, with a portion of it – named
Dun Mountain – now 500 km to the
north in Nelson. Ultramafic soils
support distinctive, stunted vegetation,
partly because they are generally stony
and shallow, but also because the high
magnesium levels are toxic
to plants. The only mineral discovered
in significant quantities in this area is
asbestos which is shunned worldwide
because of the huge health risks
associated with its mining and use.
Photo: Lloyd Homer, Geological Survey, DSIR

This was a place of rare beauty
and minerals, with rata trailing
in its sombre green forest perimeter ...
the marked change from barren desolation
to green primeval beauty is startling
to the few who have climbed
in this region.

Great Days in New Zealand Exploration, John Pascoe

Just north of Big Bay, the Cascade
Plateau separates the extensive
Hermitage swamps in the Cascade
Valley (right) from the Haast lowlands.
This unusual plateau and promontory
was formed in the last great Ice Age
by glaciers which carried infertile
ultramafic rocks from the Red Hills.
Photo: Ian Platt, DoC

Few places in the world have a rainfall
as consistently high as the South-West
– up to 14 m a year. This along
with mountain uplift and glacial
erosion, contributes to one of the
world's most unsettled landscapes.
Barely had this new hut at Welcome
Flat in the Copland Valley been
commissioned, than it was engulfed by
a huge mud slide in 1986.
Photo: Bruce Postill

Right
New Zealand's oldest
rocks are found in Fiordland.
The bluffs, Murchison Mountains,
overlooking Lake Te Anau.
Photo: Ray Joyce, Lansdowne Press

Left:

The old trench of the Tasman Glacier has now filled with millions of tonnes of gravels carried by the Tasman River. Such braided river systems provide breeding habitats for rare New Zealand birds such as the endemic black stilt and wrybill (inset).

Photos: Craig Potton

The Franz Josef Glacier plunges 2700 m from amidst New Zealand's highest peaks to only 300 m above sea level. Since last century the terminal face has retreated more than 2 km up-valley, although it is now advancing at the rapid rate of a metre a day. 20,000 years ago in the last major advance of the Ice Ages, the glacier pushed out to meet the sea well beyond the present coastline.

Photo: Craig Potton

Overleaf:

Hundreds of glaciers are found throughout the South-West. One of the more spectacular is the Douglas Glacier, a reconstituted glacier formed from ice avalanches spilling down rock precipices below Mt Sefton. The roar from ice avalanches in this inaccessible part of Westland National Park has been described as 'like that of an unending cannonade.'

Photo Gerard Hutching

Peak, ridge and pilgrim water
      still remote, untamed;
charted but all intractable,
      anonymous though named.

Basil Dowling

CHAPTER THREE

Rainforests of the South-West

A Priceless Legacy

Kevin Smith

THE INDIGENOUS vegetation of the South-West is unrivalled in New Zealand for its virgin splendour, variety and extent. Only here can we fully appreciate what this country was like before human occupation. Although forests appear to dominate the landscape from the coastline to the high peaks of the Southern Alps, a great diversity of vegetation is present.

In South Westland, the country's last extensive stands of kahikatea swamp forests can be found. Great walls of kahikatea trees line the riverbanks, a sight that was once common on New Zealand's lowland plains but is now only a fading image in the memories of some of our oldest citizens. Unique parallel formations of forested sand dunes extend along the Haast coastal plain. Open waterways, boglands and flax swamps nestle between these dunes and spread out behind them into huge wetlands that are the most extensive natural freshwater wetlands in New Zealand.

In the fiords of the glacially-gouged hard rock mountains of Fiordland, a continuous mantle of silver beech-dominant forest clings to the rain-lashed rock walls down to the very edge of the sea. On remote sandy beaches the rare native sand-binding sedge, pingao, still flourishes, away from aggressive exotic weeds. Inland, tall red beech forest, a sadly depleted forest type elsewhere, clothes the floors of eastern valleys like the Dart and Eglinton. Here, yellowheads make their last stand in this optimal habitat.

Along the southern coast, an unbroken forest canopy stretching back to the mountains of Fiordland is the crowning glory of Waitutu's extraordinary flight of marine terraces with its complex vegetation pattern of forest, woodland, shrubland and bogs.

Nature reigns supreme in this corner of New Zealand. Except for a few small enclaves of farmland in South Westland, the landscape remains overwhelmingly natural. Civilisation has been hampered by the extreme isolation, the rugged terrain, unpredictable rivers and by the stormy wet climate. The rainfall can be punishingly high. In the lowlands annual rainfall totals up to 5000 mm can be expected (though sunshine hours at Haast equal those of Christchurch); on the highest peaks of the Southern Alps, rainfall totals of 14,000 mm/year are amongst the world's highest. Under these conditions soils become sour and impoverished very quickly as over-ambitious pioneers soon discovered, and the already oversteepened mountain slopes become even more dynamic – landslides are of frequent occurrence. Yet indigenous plant life flourishes here. The wet, humid conditions and bared surfaces are rapidly revegetated. This phenomenon can give the casual observer a false impression of the dynamic nature of the land and its vegetation. For this is a region where physical upheaval from floods, landslides and frictional movements along the Alpine Fault are commonplace events today, and where ice sheets spread across much of the land not so long ago.

Far left:
New Zealand's tallest tree, and one of its rarest in extensive stands, kahikatea has been recorded as high as 60 m.
Photo: Gerry McSweeney

Inset:
Kahikatea fruit is a vital food source for birds. A mature kahikatea can produce up to 800 kg of fruit, made up of approximately 4.5 million seeds.
Photo: Gerry McSweeney

Taking a long-term view, the podocarp forests (mainly rimu and kahikatea) and to a lesser extent the beech forests, which dominate the South-West, are remarkably resilient when confronted by potentially ruinous natural events. For these are ancient forests; much older than the Southern Alps which tower over them and older than most other forests in the world. They have survived turmoil and unfavourable environments on these ever-changing islands for many millions of years.

Podocarp Forests

Podocarps belong to a very ancient family of gymnosperms. Its members were evolving and spreading across the southern plains of Gondwanaland during the Mesozoic period nearly 200 million years ago. This was the age of the dinosaur, a time when longevity and gigantism were favoured. Kahikatea, for instance, which can be traced further back into the fossil record than the other podocarps, is our tallest tree and lives for five or more centuries. Rimu has similarly ancient origins. Fossil pollen grains identical to those of the present day rimu tree occur in rocks 40 million years old.

Biologically, the dense rimu and kahikatea forests of South Westland and the dense rimu forests of Waitutu's coastal terraces are the region's singlemost outstanding feature. The South-West contains 80 percent of New Zealand's remaining unlogged dense podocarp forest.

Densely stocked kahikatea forests, with trees straight as arrows, once covered the fertile lowland river valleys and swampy plains of New Zealand. But this land was amongst the first cleared by Europeans and is now given over to dairying and horticulture. In the North Island, kahikatea is virtually extinct as a mature forest type; only in South Westland have any sizeable virgin stands of kahikatea forest survived. Even here there is only about 10,000 ha of forest where kahikatea is a dominant tree. Only 4500 ha of this is actually dense kahikatea forest.

Kahikatea is now as scarce as kauri but whereas the kauri forests are mostly protected in forest sanctuaries most of the kahikatea remains unprotected. The major kahikatea forests of South Westland are on the swampy coastal plains between Fox Glacier and Haast. Ohinetamatea, Hunts Beach, Ohinemaka and Mataketake forest contain the best stands.

Fleshy seeds adapted for bird dispersal over long distances are a distinctive feature of kahikatea and the other podocarps. Tuis, bellbirds and pigeons spread their seeds over fresh landscapes created by floods and landslides or exposed by melting ice. Of the podocarps, kahikatea is the most prolific fruiter. In a season a single kahikatea tree can produce up to 800 kg of lush purple and orange coloured fruit. This enables it to excel as a pioneering plant on the flood plains of South Westland, where rivers loaded with silt and gravels from the rising Southern Alps can abruptly swing across their flood plains, destroying forests overnight.

Kahikatea seedlings establish amidst the shrubs, grasses and sedges which colonise the raw alluvium deposited by the rivers, although today the riverflat grasslands are often maintained by stock grazing which results in a gradual diminution of the kahikatea estate.

The interaction between South Westland's big brawling rivers and kahikatea forest is dramatically illustrated in the south-west corner of Westland National Park. Here, in 1967, the lower reaches of the glacially-fed Cook River changed course and charged through the middle of a sizeable stand of kahikatea forest. On the raw silt amidst the bleached skeletons of the overwhelmed trees, a new generation of kahikatea should eventually assert itself.

Those portions of the flood plain free from frequent flooding and siltation have developed in to great kahikatea swamp forests. In places, interlocking root systems of adjacent kahikatea trees may form a platform above layers of deep peaty ooze. Often the water table is so high that the forest floor is covered by a sheet of moving water. The swamp forest regenerates itself when kahikatea seedlings establish on areas of bare mud beneath gaps in the forest canopy. Their spongy roots enable them to oxygenate their

The winter rata vine Metrosideros fulgens *is enormously important as a nectar source for honey-eating tui and bellbird through the lean winter months. This vine is confined to lowland forests into which the honeyeaters flock from the cold mountain forests in winter.*
Photo: Gerry McSweeney

The colourful mistletoe Peraxilla tetrapetala *is one of several species of mistletoe found in the South-West. Possums have destroyed this plant in many parts of New Zealand.*
Photo: Hugh Barr

Life and death of a kahikatea forest, Cook River flats, South Westland. In 1967 the Cook River changed its course from the right to left hand side of its flood plain, destroying extensive kahikatea forests. This is natural and has happened often in times past.
Photo: Tony Lilleby, DoC

rootlets and thus survive in waterlogged soils that few other trees can tolerate.

Rimu is longer lived than kahikatea; some trees can reach 800 or more years. It is also slower growing and able to tolerate poor soils. This gives rimu a competitive advantage over other trees on the older terrace surfaces where aeons of rain have leached out many nutrients and infertile podzolised soils have developed. On the terrace surfaces rimu is triumphant and can form very dense stands because it hoards nutrients in its great bulk and carefully recycles nutrients released from its litter.

On the lower terraces of Waitutu, rimu is unusually abundant in a district that is otherwise dominated by beech forests. The best developed stands occur on the glacial terraces and older alluvial surfaces of South Westland, particularly areas to the north of the beech front. Ohinemaka and Bruce Bay forests contain fine examples of dense rimu forest on post-glacial surfaces derived from old river silts. The nation's most outstanding examples of rimu forest on glacial terraces are in the South Okarito and Waikukupa forest areas of Westland National Park. Rimu is also a minor but distinctive component of Fiordland's fringe of lowland forest but is absent from all but the lower western valleys of Mt Aspiring National Park.

Seven other podocarp trees occur in the South-West region. Miro grows in similar localities to rimu and is notable for its large fruit which are dispersed by pigeon, the only living native bird able to swallow them.

Hall's totara appears in upland forests and on some of the harsher lowland sites. In the lower eastern slopes of Mt Cook National Park, remnants of Hall's totara/broadleaf forest persist in areas modified by early fires.

Matai prefers lowland sites with fertile soils, but is nowhere common. Westland National Park contains a couple of the last remnants of matai-Westland totara forest once

Celmisia inaccessa *is a rare plant which grows on vertical limestone cliffs in western Fiordland. Its name is derived from its remote location.*
Photo: Alan Mark

Buchanan's buttercup grows on rock outcrops and scree slopes south of the glaciers in Westland National Park.
Photo: Neill Simpson

Muttonbird scrub,
Olearia angustifolia *is confined to southern coastlines from southern Fiordland to Stewart Island.*
Photo: Geoff Spearpoint

common on the gravelly flood plains of Westland. Impoverished soils, such as those of the coastal plateaux of Fiordland and the higher terraces of Waitutu provide yellow silver pine and pink pine with a foothold. They are joined by silver pine on similar sites north of Martins Bay. The least unmodified stands of silver pine are in the Ohinetamatea forest. A handful of shrub podocarps are also largely restricted to these sites including the straggling pigmy pine, the smallest conifer in the world.

Beech forests

Beech, the other great forest class of New Zealand, comprises the bulk of the forests of the South-West. They too, are ancient tree species, being amongst the oldest flowering plants. Recognisable beech fossils occur in Gondwanaland deposits of early Cretaceous times, 100-135 million years ago. Scientific study of their interaction with the podocarps and of the complex distribution patterns of the individual beech species reveals the dramatic forest history of the South-West, much of it as yet untold or unknown. Because beech has a generally slow rate of spread (its seeds are only capable of limited dispersion by wind and running fresh water) its distribution gives an indication of where forest vegetation survived during the Ice Age.

Of the four beech species in the South-West, silver beech is by far the most common and widespread. It is a cold-tolerant tree found in most forested areas and on all but the most infertile soils. Throughout Waitutu, silver beech is found in mixed forests with rimu and mountain beech. In Fiordland and the Aspiring region, silver beech clothes the mountain sides from the valley bottoms to the tree line. It extends further north than the other beech species, reaching the mountain valleys of the Hooker-Landsborough and the hill country around Lakes Moeraki and Paringa. There are also remnant stands in the Hooker and Tasman Valleys of Mt Cook National Park. Apart from an outlier in the Karangarua Valley, the Mahitahi Valley marks the northern limit of silver beech in South Westland. To the north of the beech boundary lie the dense podocarp and podocarp-hardwood forests of the central portion of the West Coast. Beech forest does not reappear until the Taramakau Valley north of Hokitika.

Mountain beech attains dominance in the drier forest regions of eastern Fiordland around Manapouri and Te Anau. It is found on infertile and poorly drained sites throughout Waitutu and Fiordland but is confined to the southern valleys of Mt Aspiring National Park. A minor component of the forests in the Cascade-Haast district, it reaches its northern limit in Mataketake forest. Red beech also has an anomalous distribution. It is essentially restricted to the southern valleys of Aspiring, the mid and upper reaches of the Arawata Valley and to some of the warm fertile valleys of Fiordland such as the Eglinton. Even more puzzling is the distribution of hard beech which was only recently discovered in the region on a few low mounds on the coastal plain south of Haast between the Waiatoto and Arawata Rivers.

Anomalous distributions

The story behind such anomalous distribution patterns has been one that has fascinated forest ecologists and botanists ever since New Zealand's forests were first known to science. It is only in the South-West that the full complexity of the interplay between the beech and podocarp forests can be observed and the mysteries unravelled in an environment free from modification by forest clearance or damage from logging and fire. Only the latter chapters of the South-West forest story can be recounted and then only with some hesitancy as much of the detail is obscure. Virtually all the evidence of the early extent and abundance of forest vegetation in the region was erased by the vast ice advances of the last Ice Age.

During the height of the Ice Age very little forest could have survived. However, fossil pollen records from that time contain very small amounts of pollen from podocarps and beech trees, indicating the presence of refugia containing lowland forest plants quite near to the ice front. When the glaciers were on retreat, these refugia were crucially important life centres from which the forests were able to colonise the fresh landscapes.

We can confirm the location of forest refugia from the present day distribution of the beech species. Refugia were probably located in the southern Fiordland-Waitutu area, in the Haast-Cascade lowlands and in the largely ice-free hill country around Lakes Paringa and Moeraki. North of Paringa the ice sheets swept out to sea leaving no opportunity for forest survival. Rimu and kahikatea with their bird-dispersed seeds, would have re-established in abundance on the gravel terraces and flood plains left by the ice. However, beech trees spread so slowly they have not yet reoccupied the northern area of South Westland even though it is now 14,000 years since the end of the last glaciation.

For the first four thousand years after the glaciers began retreating shrubs and grassland continued to dominate the landscape. The onset of a wetter and milder climate about 10,000 years ago enabled the podocarps to spread rapidly across the lowlands. Beech began actively spreading only about 5000 years ago and had attained dominance with the podocarps in Fiordland about 2000 years ago. A cooler, wetter climate during this time favoured the expansion of both silver beech and rimu. Mountain beech and red beech have spread only moderate distances from possible refugia, whereas hard beech – a species that prefers free-draining infertile soils – has been hemmed in by the surrounding lowland swamp forest and has scarcely moved from its Ice Age refugia south of Haast.

The South-West is one of the best regions in the world to study the imprint of glaciation on the vegetation pattern. The area contains an exceptional diversity of impressive glacial landscapes. Recolonisation of the varied surfaces swept bare by the ice has given rise to internationally renowned examples of plant succession after glaciation. This includes the full sequence of soil surfaces from the most youthful post-glacial surfaces through mature forests to old infertile soils supporting natural low shrubland and bog vegetation. These successional sequences are best developed in Westland National Park and in the western valleys of Aspiring and the Cascade-Pyke district.

Three finger, Pseudopanax colensoi, and other sub-alpine shrubs cling precariously to the rain-lashed rock walls of Fiordland's Homer Saddle.
Photo: Gerry McSweeney

Other species

While the beech and podocarp trees form the ancient core of the forest they are, of course, accompanied by a host of other plants. The lowland forests, in particular, possess a vast assemblage of plants. Of the hardwood trees, kamahi is the most abundant and is widespread in nearly all forested areas except for the drier eastern forests. In the beech-free glacier region it shares dominance with southern rata in the montane forests. These forests are renowned for their blazing red colour in those summers when the rata is in full flower.

Several important lowland forest trees reach their southern limits on the West Coast in the glacier region, namely toro, hinau and quintinia. Common small hardwood trees and shrubs throughout the region include broadleaf, pokaka, mahoe, pate, wineberry, tree fuchsia and pigeonwood but there is tremendous variation between habitats. Tree ferns, with origins even more ancient than the podocarps, often give these cool temperate forests a subtropical appearance. In the warmer lowlands climbers such as kiekie, supplejack, climbing rata and epiphytic orchids, ferns and flowering plants can give the forest an unexpected, even tropical-like luxuriance. In the moist western forests, bryophytes are usually super-abundant, often covering the forest floor with a thick spongy carpet.

In the south, Waitutu supports a rich flora for this latitude. Over 220 species of higher plants have been recorded from its forests and a further 44 species from its grasslands.

On the coastal plains of South Westland huge wetlands interrupt the forest cover. They have formed mainly in areas innundated by rising post-glacial seas and now cut off by dune ridges. The swamps are slowly infilling from stream borne deposits from the surrounding hills. In areas where the water stagnates, infertile terrace bogs, known as pakihis, have developed. Great depths of semi-liquid peat have accumulated beneath these bogs. Flowing water creates fertile swamps which are often penetrated by sinuous flax-lined waterways. The major freshwater wetlands are the Waiuna Lagoon swamp at Big Bay; the Hermitage Swamp of the Lower Cascade Valley; the Burmeister, Waiatoto,

Okuru and Tawharekiri swamps of the Haast coastal plain; the Ohinemaka and Kini swamps at Bruce Bay and the Meyer swamp in the lower Cook River valley.

Heath and bog vegetation characterised by bog pine, dracophyllum, wire rush and umbrella fern, also occurs on impoverished mineral soils on the oldest glacial terraces in South Westland and the old marine gravel terraces on the South-West Fiordland coast. Similar vegetation covers the bleak Cascade and Gorge plateaux where only extremely hardy plants can tolerate the toxic soils on these ultramafic moraines which are derived from the ultramafic rocks (high in levels of some heavy metals as well as iron and magnesium-containing minerals) of the Red Hills. On the Red Hills themselves, specially adapted dwarfed open communities take the place of the normal vegetation on the striking rusty-red mountain slopes, and these stand out strangely and impressively from the lush green forest and tawny tussock of the surrounding country.

Kereru, the native pigeon, relies on lowland forests for food, where it finds abundant supplies of berries and fruit.
Photo: Brian Enting

Far right:
Floating forest, Hunts Beach.
Only 2 percent of New Zealand's kahikatea forests remain in unbroken stands along the plains of South Westland, in some cases literally floating on peaty ooze.
Photo: Craig Potton

Brachyglottis revolutus.
A sub-alpine shrub daisy of the boulder fields of the South-West.
Photo: Neill Simpson

Coastal vegetation

The South-West has a long and varied coastline. It offers a spectrum of habitats including rocky coastlines and their associated cliffs, river mouth estuaries and coastal lagoons, and long sweeping storm-affected gravel and sand beaches. The coastal vegetation is fascinatingly diverse but not exceptionally well developed because the high rainfall reduces the influence of salt spray. The Cascade and Fiordland coastlines are unique in New Zealand because of their pristine condition. No other coastline is as little modified by fire and introduced weeds. Rare plants such Cook's scurvy grass *(Lepidium)* and unmodified dunes of pingao occur here. Elsewhere these have been eliminated from the mainland by browsing or swamped by introduced marram grass. Limited areas of salt marsh vegetation occur at the heads of most fiords, at the river mouths and more extensively in the coastal lagoons of South Westland, the largest of which is the Okarito Lagoon.

The most obvious and ecologically significant factor influencing the vegetation pattern of the region is altitude. There is a range of natural altitudinal sequences stretching from the coast and lowland river flats to mountain peaks above the limit of vegetation.

In Westland lowland forest is restricted to country below 400 m above sea level; this is mainly the alluvial plains and glacial moraines west of the Alpine Fault. Here, rimu has an upper altitudinal limit of 600 m and extends into the lower montane forest. In Fiordland, rimu rarely occurs above 450 m but only in Waitutu are there any sizeable areas of easy terrain below this height.

Generally, simpler montane forest (rata and kamahi in the northern part of South Westland and silver beech forest elsewhere) extends above the lowland forest to the treeline of gnarled stunted trees at 800-1000 m, depending on latitude and distance from the coast. Above the treeline alpine shrublands and tussock grasslands are in turn replaced by herbfields and rocky fellfields. The upper limit of vegetation varies from 1500 to 2000 m. One of the distinctive botanical features of the Southern Alps is its alpine flora. Like the mountains they grow on, the alpine plants are of more recent origin than the podocarps or beeches.

The low-alpine vegetation is characterised by snow tussocks up to a metre tall near treeline. These shelter mountain daises (*Celmisia* spp), buttercups (*Ranuculus* spp), foxgloves (*Ourisia* spp), lilies (*Astelia* spp), and many other alpine herbs. Most famous of these is the showy and highly palatable *Ranunculus lyallii* (the great mountain buttercup or Mt Cook 'lily'). In the high-alpine belt, a smaller number of herbs, sedges, mosses and lichens form an intermittent cover amidst rock and permanent snow. Introduced wild herbivores (deer, chamois, thar) have been drastically reduced over the last two decades by commercial hunters using helicopters, and the alpine vegetation and flora is now returning to something like its original glory as relayed by the early explorers.

Pterostylis banksii, *a greenhood orchid of the native forest floor.*
Photo: J H Harding

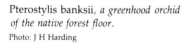

Summary of Botanical Features of International Importance

The South-West region contains the most extensive lowland native forests remaining in New Zealand and are a representative example of temperate rainforests of global importance. The lowland podocarp rainforests are of international scientific interest as the most significant modern representatives of the ancient forests of the Mesozoic era.

The region contains outstanding examples of plant succession after glaciation, covering extended chronological sequences from fresh post-glacial surfaces to old moraines including the only ultramafic moraines in the world.

The beech-podocarp ecotone in South Westland is the only complete unmodified example where the complex process of forest readjustment after glaciation is represented in New Zealand.

The region contains the best and most complete altitudinal zonation patterns encompassing virtually the full range of forest and non-forest communities of Southern New Zealand.

The region contains the most extensive remaining natural freshwater wetlands and estuarine systems in New Zealand.

Many unique, distinctive and nationally important plants and plant associations occur within the South-West region.

The area contains the most extensive remaining kahikatea forest in New Zealand. Now reduced to about 2 per cent of its original extent, the coastal lowlands of southern South Westland are the last remaining stronghold of this important forest type in the country.

The Poison Bay – Transit area of Fiordland contains some of the last native forest on mainland New Zealand virtually unaffected by the browsing of introduced mammals.

The area includes the total population of the endangered tussock grass Chionochloa spiralis *which is confined to calcareous rubble in a small area of Fiordland.*

Many other alpine plants are endemic to the region.

Mt McLean and the Arawata River mouth. South-West vegetation reflects its landforms. The granite mound of Mt McLean escaped later glaciations; scattered among its silver beech-clad slopes can be found one of a handful of refuges for hard beech in southern New Zealand. Around its slopes the rimu and kahikatea forests of the Haast lowlands are densest on well drained soils alongside rivers. Further back the forest covers the raised marine beaches while the depressions between support deep peat swamps.
Photo: Ian Platt, DoC

Above left:

To the north, silver beech is also the dominant species in Mt Aspiring National Park and the Landsborough Valley. The scenic Haast highway traverses this magnificent forest landscape.

Photo: Gerry McSweeney

Above right:

Rimu-beech forests cover the marine terraces of Waitutu, the largest tract of unmodified lowland native forest in New Zealand. Elsewhere farming has taken its toll on flood plain beech but these still survive unmodified alongside the Wairaurahiri River.

Photo: Chris Ward

Left:

Matai-totara alluvial forest is an endangered forest type, although it was once common on the stony flood plains throughout New Zealand. Today less than one thousandth remains, virtually all of it in South Westland.

Photo: Craig Potton

Cold-tolerant silver beech forest clothes the steep mountainsides of Fiordland, down to the ocean edge. The history of New Zealand's beech forests can be traced back more than 100 millions years to Gondwanaland, and today their relatives are found in Tasmania and South America.

Photo: Craig Potton

Below:

Sub-alpine vegetation, Hump Ridge, Waitutu. The bronze-tinted Dracophyllum menziesii and flowering Celmisia contrast with the yellow coloured tussock.

Photo: Les Molloy

Scabweed, mosses and grasses colonise sands and gravels below the terminal of Westland's Horace Walker Glacier in the first stage of plant succession to forest.
Photo: Gerry McSweeney

Snow-clad beech and mountain ribbonwood, Fiordland. Gnarled silver beech forms the bushline through much of Fiordland. In particularly cold hollows and valleys grows mountain ribbonwood, one of New Zealand's few deciduous trees.
Photo: D Comer

Red Algae. In most of the world algae – seaweed – is confined to water but so high is the rainfall west of the Southern Alps it actually grows on rocks, fences and posts.
Photo: A. Reith

Overleaf:
Kahikatea swamp forest.
Photo: Craig Potton

A forest land of deep shade
and tangled growth ...
a land of silence and mystery
save for the voice
of many waters. Maud Moreland.

CHAPTER FOUR

A Wildlife Haven

Animals of the South-West

Colin O'Donnell

ABOUT 136 MILLION years ago, as New Zealand began its separation from the supercontinent Gondwanaland, the ancestors of the kiwi and moa also floated off on this landmass.

Already flightless, they prefigured a process of evolutionary change that would see New Zealand become host to a number of unique animals, often described as 'evolutionary relics' – direct descendants of ancestral types that in other parts of the world have been replaced by more recently evolved forms. Most spectacular of all were the birds, but equally important were the land snails, bats and lizards.

In successive waves following this separation from Gondwanaland, different bird species colonised New Zealand. Most ancient were the kiwi and moa, followed by the wattlebirds, wrens and thrushes about 60 million years ago. Closer to the present day, rails such as the takahe and parrots such as the kakapo arrived.

South-West New Zealand, the least modified region on the mainland, is today the final stronghold for a number of these colonists. As such it is of world significance.

More than 100 species of birds have been recorded in the South-West, more than half of the species that breed in New Zealand. This diversity is guaranteed by the variety of the habitats: the sea coast, estuaries and lagoons, swamplands and bogs, meandering and braided rivers, lakes, forest sequences from lowland to high altitudes, and the alpine zone.

The Habitats

Blue penguins, Fiordland crested penguins, sooty shearwaters, broad-billed prion and the fairy prion breed in the impenetrable coastal scrub and stunted forests along the South-West's rugged coast. Another oceanic species, the rare mottled petrel, also nests around the Fiordland coast. Southern skuas, gulls, white-fronted terns, reef herons and blue shags nest on rock stacks, in caves and on islets off the coast while pied shag colonies occur at some rivermouths.

Okarito Lagoon is justly famous for being the site of the only white heron breeding colony in New Zealand. Here a complex of swamp, estuarine mudflats and open water forms the largest habitat of its type along the South Island's west coast. The kotuku breeds north of the lagoon near the mouth of the Waitangiroto River, nesting in the tall kahikatea trees or the kamahi and kowhai which overhang the water. To the Maori, the kotuku symbolises everything rare and beautiful. Only about 100 of them breed at Okarito. Royal spoonbills also breed at the mouth of the Waitangiroto, one of three breeding sites in New Zealand.

Okarito is a haven for other bird life. Surveys have shown that at times about half of the South Island pied oystercatchers, variable oystercatchers, bar-tailed godwits and knots of the South-West region are on the lagoon.

In the northern half of the South-West, from Okarito south to Big Bay, pakihi bog is a valuable habitat covering thousands of hectares. Umbrella fern, rushes, sedges, flax and raupo provide a home to many wetland birds, including fernbirds, bittern, and spotless

Far left:
Te Kotuku-rerenga-tahi. 'The rare white heron of a single flight'. The kotuku or white heron has always been rare in New Zealand with a total population of about 100 birds. It breeds only at the Waitangiroto sanctuary north of Okarito Lagoon, then disperses to estuaries and wetlands throughout New Zealand.
Photo: P & J Morrin

crake. Elsewhere in New Zealand drainage has spelled the doom of these secretive wetland species. Open ponds amongst this pakihi bog are inhabited by the endangered brown teal and little and black shags often breed in overhanging trees.

Two types of river occur in the South-West. West of the Southern Alps they are typically single channel, running through high country torrents into deep meandering rivers in the lowlands. Blue duck occur in the mountains and herons and shags in the lowlands.

Braided rivers such as the Haast and Arawata on the West Coast and the Tasman and Dart on the east are rare internationally. More than 30 bird species live and breed on these, including the wrybill, black-fronted tern and black-billed gull.

Throughout the South-West are dotted some of New Zealand's largest lakes – Te Anau, Manapouri, Poteriteri, Hauroko. Two species in particular are dependent on them – the endangered southern crested grebe and the New Zealand scaup. With its glossy back plumage and brilliant diving skills, the scaup stands apart from other ducks.

Of the more than 40 bird species found in the South-West's forests, the majority are found only in New Zealand. Parakeet, tui, New Zealand pigeon, robin and most introduced birds are encountered more often in the low altitude and coastal forests. In the higher altitude rata-kamahi forests to the north and the silver beech-dominant forests to the south, kaka, kea, brown creeper, long-tailed cuckoo and rifllemen are more common. Found throughout are the bellbird, yellow-breasted tit, grey warbler, fantail and silvereye.

The alpine zone is the least hospitable of environments and consequently bird numbers are low. Dense stands of alpine scrub provide habitat for tits, warblers, riflemen, finches, dunnocks, blackbirds and the occasional falcon. In the Landsborough Valley kaka venture into the alpine zone when nectar is available on inaka, hakeke and lacebark bushes.

Still higher, herbfields are the typical haunt of the kea, the only alpine parrot in the world. The rock wren is New Zealand's only true alpine bird and is found throughout the region. The wren spends the whole winter in the mountains, remaining under a blanket of snow and feeding in the air spaces between shrubs and boulders.

Other Wildlife

The South-West supports a unique assemblage of other wildlife: insects, land snails, lizards, one endemic bat, large colonies of fur seals and native freshwater fish. Very little is known about most groups and many invertebrates have yet to be named.

Four species of carnivorous *Powelliphanta* land snails occur in the South-West. While not as large as their northern counterparts they are still impressive. They have been seen mostly in high altitude silver beech where they live in the forest litter and at the base of shield ferns.

One of New Zealand's two native bats, the long-tailed, is a relatively recent immigrant from Australia, presumably blown across the Tasman by westerly storms. This bat favours living in holes in kahikatea trees.

Few of the skinks and geckos sighted in the South-West have been identified. However, one skink, *Leiolopisma acrinasum*, or the Fiordland skink lives in arguably the harshest climatic conditions of all the skink family – on the exposed coast around Breaksea Sound in Fiordland where it is frequently showered with salt water and spray.

Most of New Zealand's fur seals are found along the South-West coast. Between 1792 and 1830 the species was virtually wiped out but since then they have made a comeback, now numbering about 50,000 throughout the country.

Freshwater Fish

The complex mosaic of swamps, lakes and rivers in the South-West, unrivalled anywhere else in New Zealand, provides an abundance of habitats for native freshwater fish. Recent surveys have shown that more than a dozen species of freshwater fish live in the region, including the giant kokopu, largest galaxiid in the world, the scarce short-jawed kokopu, eel and whitebait.

Tales of whitebait catching have taken on mythical proportions on the West Coast, where the delicacy occurs in its greatest numbers. Fisheries scientists rate the Cascade River, just below the township of Haast, as the most important whitebait river in New Zealand. The average catch in the Cascade of the small galaxiid is 23 million fish per season, about half the total whitebait catch for New Zealand.

The international values of the South-West for wildlife are clear. The region is not only a refuge for many of our endangered animals, most of which are unique in world terms, it is also an area where more common species can continue to thrive without threat of development. Given world heritage status, the South-West should remain as a haven for New Zealand's distinctive species.

South-West New Zealand offers an array of diverse habitats for the wildlife of the region: coastline, estuary and lagoon, swampland, river, lake, forest scrub and scree. Coastal lagoon, Waita River, South Westland.
Photo: Craig Potton

Two of New Zealand's three kiwi species occur in the South-West. The great spotted kiwi is rare, scattered along the main alpine chain from Franz Josef south to at least the Arawata Valley. More numerous, the brown kiwi (pictured) occurs in three distinct populations, each showing genetic differences resulting from centuries of isolation. A small population is found in South Okarito forest and another between the Haast and Arawata Rivers. There is a more extensive population in Fiordland.
Photo: DoC

One of New Zealand's smallest birds, the alpine-dwelling rock wren is a bird of ancient lineage. It often spends the winter months snowbound beneath rock outcrops.
Photo: C R Veitch, DoC

Right:
In the South-West the kaka is still found in large social flocks, but like many of our forest birds elsewhere in New Zealand it has disappeared from much of its former range because of bush clearance. Waitutu and southern South Westland lowland forests contain New Zealand's highest remaining kaka populations.
Photo: P Daniel

Whio or blue duck is a torrent duck,
specially adapted to feeding in river
rapids. Once found in their thousands
in the South-West, about 1890 their
numbers declined drastically, with stoats,
ship rats and riverside forest clearance
responsible for their demise.
Today blue duck still occur in low
numbers in most of the South-West's
mountain streams.
Photo: A Reith

Kakapo were once abundant throughout New Zealand, but today there are possibly only about 10 in Fiordland, all of them males, with the largest population of 40 on Stewart Island. The world's largest parrot, it long ago lost virtually all its powers of flight.
Photo: DoC

A female tomtit. An insect-eating member of the robin family, the tomtit is widespread and easily seen throughout the South-West because of its lack of fear of people.
Photo: P & J Morrin

One of New Zealand's two native mammals, the long-tailed bat is found in kahikatea forests where it nests in holes formed in the tree's soft wood.
Photo: Tony Whitaker

One of the hardiest of the world's skinks is the Fiordland skink, which lives around Fiordland's exposed coast. It is able to swim underwater for several minutes.
Photo: Tony Whitaker

Stick Insect.
Photo: Gerry McSweeney

The highlight for many tourists
to the South-West is an encounter
with the playful kea – our cheeky
mountain parrot. Although naturally a
vegetarian, the world's only alpine
parrot has developed a taste for food
handouts from tourists who meet it at
such places as Fox Glacier, Mt Cook
and on the Routeburn and
Milford tracks.
Photo: Snow Bain, Post Office

Along hundreds of kilometres of
the South-West coastline, numerous
seabirds such as the shy (white-capped)
mollymawk breed and live.
Photo: Wynston Cooper

Just as worthy of protection as the South-West's land inhabitants are the special underwater animals of Fiordland. However, the National Park boundary extends only to the water's edge. This one metre tall black coral colony supports several perching snake stars. The largest colony of black coral in the world (although it appears white) occurs in the fiords.

Photo: Ken Grange

The tube anemone is very common throughout the fiords in sandy pockets below 6 m, but rare elsewhere in New Zealand.

Photo: Roger Grace

The fiords are the only place in the world where a diver will come across a sea pen. Everywhere else these grow at extreme depths. However, low light levels in the peat-stained fiord waters enable normally deep water animals to live in shallow areas. Height 30cm.

Photo: Roger Grace

The South-West is special for its continuity of habitats – from lowland swamps and lakes through extensive lowland forests to the colder, simpler forests of the mountainsides. Studies of bird populations in the flax encircled kahikatea forests of South Westland shown here have found a four-fold increase in winter as the birds move down from the mountain forests.
Photo: Les Molloy

Whitebait is a fish delicacy increasingly difficult to find today as its swamp breeding grounds are drained for farming and forestry. The inanga (adult whitebait) is pictured.
Photo: Tony Eldon

CHAPTER FIVE

Te Whenua Whai-Taoka

Keri Hulme

THERE IS an old whakatauki, an old proverb, that goes

E raro, rawa kore: e runga, tini hanga.
In the north, sparseness: in the south, plentitude.

South-West New Zealand is a green world, full of riches. It has a mild climate, albeit slightly damp. In the forests, anciently, were vast numbers of birds – kakapo, kiwi, bush moa and weka, as well as the delectable, though smaller, kereru, tui and kaka. Ducks abounded in lagoon areas, and were easily rounded up during their moult. The streams and rivers swarmed with eels and koura, young lamprey, inaka, and upokororo. In the estuaries and lakes, were freshwater mussels, flounders, and along the sea coasts, crabs and kina, toretore and paua, limpets and mussels and pipi and cockles, pupu and tuatua and the Coarse Dosinia . . . and the sea fish! Shark, ling, kahawai, groper, cod, mackerel, barracouta. . .

Nor was there a shortage of wild vegetable food. Fern curls and aruhe; raupo 'flour' and its young shoots (called karito, from whence 'Okarito' – a good place to gather that food); fungi and puha and the enormous harvests from podocarp trees. The sweet pith of mamaku was a favourite food-to-be, and the ti would yield a root with the same carbohydrate value as kumara, but 15 times the fat.

Seaweeds were to be collected and eaten, seals harvested; penguins, dolphins, and the occasional stranded whale to be relished (and more than the occasional stranded human). Titi chicks, succulent with fat. . .

Food there was in seasonal plenty, an abundance of riches.

And in the forests, great trees for constructing waka, and on the forest margins, more than a sufficiency of flax and kiekie and tikumu and lacebark to go into clothing. And stones for tools, weaponry, and adornment. Takiwai; pounamu. . .

The land invited people: the people came.

He wahi waimarie

The 10th century, as far as historical time goes, is probably the latest date that Polynesian people made themselves a home on Tai Poutini, the greenstone coast. It may have been very much earlier – Ngahue, an ancestral figure from the deeps of time, was pursued by the green fish Poutini, a son of Takaroa, sent after him by a deserted wife, according to legend. Ngahue almost certainly took back to his homeland sufficient of Poutini's flesh – pounamu, greenstone – to make the archaic and wondrous adzes that helped construct the great canoes which brought the Maori to Aotearoa.

The people were not known as 'Maori', then. Nga Tini o Rapuwai, the multitudes of Rapuwai, who explored the Murihiku end of Te Wahi Pounamu, who fired a lot of forest

Far left:
Maoris responded imaginatively to the wonders of the South-West. Horo Koau (Mt Tasman), standing tall above the Fox Glacier's ice fall, was said to represent a shag drying its wings.
Photo: Craig Potton

and butchered most of the moa, certainly were present on the western coasts. They were followed by other tribes and hapu – Kati Wairaki, Kati Mamoe, Waitaha, Poutini Kai Tahu, Kati Tama. . .

Tribe succeeded tribe, sometimes through warfare, though

'In fact, there is no archaelogical evidence of warfare in the south until about the 17th century' (Atholl Anderson),

sometimes, through intermarriage: the whakapapa of the south and west show the continuing links.

South-western New Zealand was not – as is often stated – just a haven for refugees from battlegrounds, and stragglers from Murihiku. It was not a place where languished the melancholy remnants of proud but beaten peoples, 'Lost Tribes'. People settled there in relatively large numbers, as well as travelling to the area to garner its riches.

The travellers to Tai Poutini and Mahitahi came by two means – feet, and sea & river vessels (the people who settled, moved round the same way, naturally enough! Although there is one tantalising story of a character who made a giant kite. . .). On foot, over the alpine passes, traversing the forests, crossing the many rivers; by sea, round the sullen-straited and treacherous tip of the South Island.

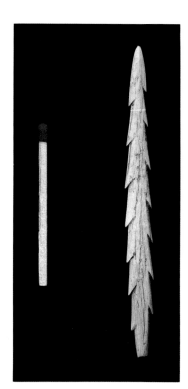

A bone bird spear found in a midden at Bruce Bay.
Photo: Ian Platt, DoC

The sea-farers used double-hulled waka, waka-huhunu, powered by sail and paddle (though there is a tradition that the people of the far south were using a kind of oar before Europeans arrived: short of recovering an anciently-dated oar, there is probably no way of proving this.) The land-farers protected their feet with sandals (paraerae of various kinds, made of ti or flax leaves that had been heated and dried to stiffness, then plaited into not-very-durable footwear). They protected their calves with tough woven leggings; crossed the rivers in craft called mokihi, made of bundles of raupo, (and identical to boats made in North Africa and Peru).

Both kinds of travellers wore kilts and cloaks and maro. Cloaks were made of wekaskins sewn together, of elegantly-joined strips of dogskin, of tikumu thatched against the rain (and sometimes lined with the inner bark of lacebark, beaten to make a tapa-like cloth). Sealskins were probably also used, although there is no evidence of this, and little traditional authority.

They carried preserved foods to supplement what they could gather on the journey – dried shark and eel and inaka; dried mamaku and fernroot. They took with them dogs, as travelling companions and hunting assistants; as hotwater bottles for the nights; as possible cloaks; as potential meals at any time.

While there were hazards on all routes – avalanche and rockfalls and sudden snowstorms in the high country, rough and changeable rivers and seas – travelling wasnt uncommon.

'Ngai Tahu were much given to travelling about, both by sea and land.' (Harry Evison)

You travelled because you wanted tokaihaukai (engage in gift-exchange) or you wanted to trade, or you planned a little exciting war, or you wanted to collect something that wasnt available in your area, or you just wanted a change of scenery and some fresh gossip. There was room and time for such travelling, and often the means to do it.

Te oranga o te takata, he whenua
When the people werent travelling, they lived a seasonally ordered life. The year began with the rising of Pipiri, the winter-heralding star. April was the month to hopu titi (catch and process the young chicks of the sooty shearwater). July was the time for wekas. In August, the tui and the kaka were especially fat, while September and October were good times for harvesting whitebait and kanakana. November for eels, and December for

starting to store food away. February was the best time to make poha-rimu (for storage), and then it was Pipiri again.

Inbetweentimes, clothing was made, and nets and cordage and hooks. Whata were constructed to store the food, and whare to store the people overnight (housing changed according to climatic conditions and need; Boultbee, writing in the 1820's, describes typical Murihiku whare thus:

'Some of them are 30 feet long; they are built of bark or reeds placed between rows of horizontal rods of wood. The walls are about 2 feet high, but the roofs are lofty, being nearly 20 feet from the wallplate to the ridgepole which is placed in a slanting direction, the highest end being next to the gable end where the door is, in order that the smoke may have freer egress; the fires are made at the furtherest extremity of the house: on each side are platforms of a species of bamboo, which are elevated about 3 feet from the ground; on these the people sleep, or sit at work when they are making mats etc. The passage between the platforms is about 2 feet, and extends the length of the house. The roofs, especially if made of reeds, soon acquire a shining black colour, from constant smoke of the fires.')

Instant shelter-houses were described by the earliest European observers: there are traditions, as yet unconfirmed by archaeological evidence, of rounded whare in the south-west, and houses partially sunken into the ground.

Waka were made (traditionally,. Bruce Bay – Here-taniwha – was known as a canoe factory), and tools and weaponry.

He mahi kai hoaka, he mahi kai takata
They were not a long-lived people, for all the riches that were available to them. After

Okarito village, once the site of a Maori village. The area near here was valuable for food, with large bird populations, shellfish and fish in the nearby lagoons and ocean. Okarito itself means 'the place of raupo'; the processed pollen heads of this plant were a succulent food.
Photo: Ian Platt, DoC

'Ko te Tau-tea ka tu'—
the white thread fixed against the cliff.

Kiekie, used for clothes and weaving, grows luxuriantly in the South-West.
Photo: Gerard Hutching

The Te Anau-Milford Sound overland trail was used by Maoris to reach the much sought-after Anita Bay greenstone, or takiwai (tangiwai). Along the way they passed the Sutherland Falls (Te Tau-tea), highest in New Zealand and one of the highest in the world.
Photo: Lloyd Homer, Geological Survey, DSIR

what seems to have been a climatic change in the 12/13th centuries (which may have accounted for rising seas, and the decline of sand-dwelling shellfish – prominent in southwestern middens, but almost non-existent now), and the decrease of the moa populations (undoubtedly from over-hunting), life became less easy.

Going by the skeletons found to date, the old people had an average life span of 30-35 years. They died from effects of jaw abcesses, they died from a particularly revolting kind of leprosy, they died with joints and spines eroded by sheer hard work. While they were old at forty, I dont think they were eager for death then. For these were people who sang a welcome to each rising sun, who mourned its nightly decline with softer, sadder songs. These were people who fed each major rising star with ceremonial fires and especial words, people who told each other ancient stories, and composed intricate song-poems to mark those momentous human events we all share in – births, and the griefs and pleasures of love, torments, and deaths.

Serendipity Cave tools, found just south of Jackson Bay. Evidence uncovered in the last few years has revealed that permanent Maori settlements existed along the South Westland coast of a greater size and scope than was previously believed.
Photo: Ian Platt, DoC

They may have been worn out early by harsher living than we are accustomed to – worn out in the same way that the hard work of shaping pounamu with sandstone wears out both sandstone and worker (and wears down the pounamu! the whakatauki heading this section can be used in many different ways) – but their lives had a depth and a richness and a worthwhileness that many of us are denied today.

He iti ra, he iti mapihi pounamu

Most New Zealanders still have something in common with the old people however – a love and desire for greenstone. The very earliest inhabitants were not interested in pounamu. Their tools were made from argillite, silcrete, basalt and obsidian; their ornaments were made from whale and moa bones, teeth, and shells.

But the beauty and durability of pounamu were quickly recognised and exploited. And while other sources of the stone were known (Central Otago, and the Arahura and Marsden areas, for examples), Okahu and Wakatipu and the Cascade area were prime collecting places. Takiwai – which some of the old people actually prized more highly than greenstone – is found only in the South-West.

These adzes made from argillite – sourced in Nelson or Southland – point to the fact that Maoris of South Westland traded valuable stone with tribes from other regions.
Photo: Ian Platt, DoC

Neither stone was generally taken off the Coast in rough as-found form. Pounamu was worked – flaked and hammerdressed originally, into slab adzes or finished ornaments, weapons, or tools until Kai Tahu technology introduced the less wasteful, though more laborious, process of shaping that very tough stone by wearing away at it with hoaka and water and people–power. Trade caches of adzes have been found here, and South Westland pounamu has turned up in the furthermost North. And the presence of Otakou porcellanite, Coromandel obsidian, and argillite from Nelson in the South-West bears witness to the extensive trade links that existed formerly – trade based on that treasured material, that fish Poutini, pounamu.

Toitu he kaika, whatu ngarongaro he takata

It is always there, the land. O, not unchanged: earthquakes happen, and there are avalanches of rock and mud, and the sea raids the shore. What dwells on land, changes too. The moa is gone: too much of Te-maranui-o-Tane has been felled and cleared. Here, people came, people flourished; people fail, other people come. But the land, and whatever riches it supports, are the constancy. People are, by comparison, ephemeral.

By the 1850s, Maori occupation of the South-West was limited. Kati Toa and Kati Tama raiding had driven some people away, and increasing Pakeha encroachment displaced others. A decade later, thousands and thousands of gold-hungry migrants arrived at Okarito and places further south. There were still substantial Maori settlements at Makawhio and Here-taniwha, but less of a presence than there had ever been before, since humans arrived on the Greenstone Coast.

Pingao was a valued weaving plant for the Maori; the South-West contains extensive stands in areas like Sandhill Point, Waitutu.
Photo: Gerry McSweeney

While the new arrivals from Europe and elsewhere found a myriad of traces of relatively recent occupation – whata, and whare posts, at Whanganui and Okarito; extensive cultivations at Porangirangi; a drowned kaika near the Poherua, and adzes and ornaments in many places – there was little else left. Wood and bone are quickly eaten by weather, and rats, and birds, and borers. Mature-looking forest can re-establish itself quickly here: within a century or so, a lay person would think nothing has been touched, all is virgin territory, nobody has *ever* lived here. Only stone . . . persists.

Recent archaeological excavation has uncovered evidence of greenstone flake-factories; of small hearthplaces probably used for anti-sandfly fires (ngaio and kawakawa smoked on them); of middens that finally establish both the presence of a large and settled population, and that population's ability to catch great quantities of offshore fish.

Much more archaeological work remains to be done. South Island Maori are confident such work will eventually bear out our ancestors orally-transmitted traditions of ancient and populous kaika throughout this area.

One thing is already certain: our ancestors handed on to us a gift, a rich and splendid land called Mahitahi. That land has fed and clothed and housed and comforted us for over a thousand years, yet it has not been devastated by us. The establishment of World Heritage status for the southwestern part of New Zealand means that other peoples besides the takata whenua, other peoples, whether they be Pakeha, or visitors to New Zealand, or members of the latest heke tohere (from both the North Island and the East Coast of Te Wahi Pounamu), other people can share our riches – the spiritual dimension of Te Maranui o Tane, the feast for the eyes, the balm for the soul, the relaxation of body&mind contained here in the south. Other people can share our riches, for they are now more than ours, a heritage for all the world.

Kia ora tatou katoa.

CHAPTER SIX

From Exploitation to Appreciation

200 Years of European Settlement

Craig Potton

PARADOXICALLY this wild South Westland landscape which provided for comparatively few Maori and today contains a sparse population, once harboured more Europeans than all the rest of New Zealand. Europeans discovered the region in the early 1800s during a period of world wide colonial plunder of natural commodities. Here the resources were seals, whales and gold. The peaking and dying off of each wave of exploitation came with the speed and brevity of skyrockets, and in just a few decades the whales and seals were driven to the very brink of extinction and the easy gold removed. Most people moved on and the center of 'progress' in this British colony shifted away from South Westland never to return.

On 13 December 1642, Dutch navigator, Abel Janzoon Tasman described the Southern Alps from the sea as 'a large land uplifted high' but he made no landfall, quickly departing north in a course of least resistance to the prevailing westerly gales. As in so many other places in the Pacific it was the great English navigator, James Cook who was the first European to explore parts of this region in detail. From 1769 onwards he made several trips to the southern fiords spending most time in the shelter of Dusky Sound. Here he rested his men, repaired his ship and in his usual thorough manner made extensive recordings of the landscape and wildlife as well as charting the seaways.

Sealing

The first sealing gang was landed in the fiords in 1792, ushering in a period of ruthless exploitation. Hundreds of thousands of defenseless seals were clubbed to death over the next 25 years, until they were all but exterminated, only to be replaced by the southern right whale as the prime target. This was an unusual period of exploration in that newly discovered areas and sealing grounds were cloaked in secrecy rather than trumpeted out in glory. However, slowly but surely the fiords were individually explored and given European names culminating in a thorough hydrological survey of the region in 1850 by Captain Stokes on board H.M.S. Acheron. Stokes predicted Fiordland would be spared the worst of exploitation simply because of its rugged terrain with 'not enough soil to nourish a potato'.

An early surveyor, Adam Johnston, described one of its fiords as 'a safe retreat for the distressed mariner, or where the man of science can retire for a while and examine into the mysteries of nature; and where the tourist can wander among scenes of beauty and grandeur which may be paralleled but hardly excelled.'

Exploration

The fiords which had provided bounty and shelter for those who travelled by sea were the most inhospitable prospect for the new settlers exploring the South Island's interior. In

Far left:
The Landsborough River, sweeping 60 km south from Mt Cook, is a wilderness mecca, and along with the region around Mt Hooker forms the remote Hooker-Landsborough Wilderness area. Looking across Marks Flat to Mt Hooker.
Photo: Hugh Barr

fact none of the area from Mt Cook and Franz Josef to the southern tip of Fiordland held good hopes of agricultural land for settlement. Provincial governments and chambers of commerce sent out explorers like Thomas Brunner, who walked for 18 months from Nelson down the West Coast to the Paringa River and back in 1847/8 and the exuberant naturalist and romantic, Julius Von Haast from Christchurch, who was in the same region in the late 1850s and exploring the glaciers around Mt Cook in 1862. Surveyor John Turnball Thomson, Nathanael Chalmers, Alphonese Barrington and others worked inland from Dunedin and Invercargill in the late 1850s discovering tussock pasturage and huge lakes before encountering the massive mountain chain of the Southern Alps that barred all westward prospect.

Although explorers like Julius Von Haast had an unbridled curiosity and passion for exploration and were struck with awe by the beauty of the discoveries of their journeys, their reports were less than encouraging to their pragmatic superiors. They were, after all in the paid employment of a new colony to which every magnificent mountain of greywacke and schist presented a useless, unusable obstacle. Samuel Butler expressed, with irony, the dominant view of the time: 'I am forgetting myself into admiring a mountain which is of no use for sheep. This is wrong. A mountain here is only beautiful if it has good grass on it.'

Just when it was becoming painfully clear to the new colonies that vast inland plains of good pasture were but lost dreams of false rumours, (excepting the obvious tussock lands around the Southern Lakes District) the most seductive lure of all appeared. Gold was found and fought for from Port Preservation in the south to Okarito in the north. In the early 1860s people flooded into South Westland. During the gold rushes settlement was densely concentrated along coastal rivermouths, beach sands and foredunes. Townships like Okarito, 5 Mile and Gillespies Beach grew from the bush overnight, each attaining populations of several thousand at their peaks. Yet gold is a fickle mistress and within two years Okarito and the other towns were all but abandoned to the gorse and regenerating forest – a symbol of the boom and bust character of resource exploitation in Westland. Today all that remains of these boom towns are a few rusting edifices that were once gold dredges and waterways for sluicing.

Although the time of the gold boom was short its effects were profound. New Zealanders were made suddenly aware of the forgotten corner of their country and intense exploration in fine detail occurred at breakneck speed. Charlie Douglas, an extraordinary Westland explorer, wrote: 'The southern parts of Westland were overhauled by bands of men who in the hunt after Gold feared neither death nor the Devil…they boldly penetrated forest and mountain, crossed rivers and scrambled around bluffs.' Gold prospectors – the likes of Patrick Caples, Charles Cameron, and others were the first

Fur seals, Fiordland coast. The early Europeans who came to New Zealand swiftly left a sorry legacy in their wake, virtually wiping out the mainland fur seal population. Since sealing ceased in 1946, however, total New Zealand fur seal numbers have climbed back to more than 50,000, concentrated around southern coasts and outlying islands.
Photo: D Comer

Far left:
Gold fever in the 1860s saw townships spring up overnight along the West Coast, but in a few short years the rush was over. Okarito was the largest gold town of the South-West.
Photo: A Reith

Left:
Gold was found in rivers and fine black sand along the coasts. However at Preservation Inlet, Fiordland, it was mined from quartz reef.
Photo: Craig Potton

European explorers to discover passes and routes throughout much of South Westland and Fiordland. Their routes became pack tracks; some of which would later form the basis of roads and other walking tracks. Ports were established on river bars and trading began in a landscape that otherwise would never have been settled. It was to supply the diggers' many needs that sawmills were set up, the bush cleared and farms developed on the riverflats. Farmers and sawmillers, (often themselves ex-prospectors), remained after those chasing the gold had long ago dispersed and but for the tourist operators, deerhunters and crayfishermen of Fiordland it is their ancestors who make up the small population living in South Westland today.

Tourism

However, after 50 years of boom-bust exploitation in a landscape that repeatedly failed to provide for the exploiters' dreams, a more subtle use of the land gained ascendancy. Charlie Douglas, an extraordinary explorer, who charted virtually every South Westland river valley and range north of Fiordland in the 1890s, realised along with a few other shrewd observers that the most profitable exploitation of South Westland lay in the preservation of the land: 'The mines they intend to develop in the future is the gold and silver in the pockets of the tourists. No more roads for diggers but tracks to waterfalls and glaciers.'

Gentlemen climbers from the British Alpine Club and other Victorian tourists with stout hearts and a romantic vision began to seek out these wild and far flung corners of the earth for inspiration from their awesome natural beauty. Local goldmen like Peter and Alex Graham turned from shovels to ice picks and led the new seekers to pristine lakes and bush-clad river valleys, glaciers and high peaks. During the 1880s the now famous Milford Track was opened and the assault on the high mountains began in earnest. Each settlement on the fringe of the lakes, fiords and mountains developed its own tourist and guiding tradition with large wooden hotels set amongst idyllic alpine environments. Great climbs were done and duly recorded in adventure books which sold well in the cities and back in Europe, along with magnificent watercolour paintings and large plate photos. At times this early appreciation of scenic New Zealand captured a rather unreal 'picturesque' atmosphere. However, it was undoubtedly these efforts which brought a new colony, and its motherland, to recognise the aesthetic and economic values of New Zealand's wilderness.

By the 1880s the first small reserves had been created around Mt Cook and in 1905, 930,480 ha of Fiordland were set aside as a public reserve. These acts of protection were soon followed by a series of reserves around the lakes and glaciers of South Westland (1911). However, it took the young colony some 50 years for these initial moves and further extensions to be consolidated into a comprehensive National Parks Act in 1952. During this time a growing national pride in wild places led to pressure for further preservation.

What had been the tourist mecca for a few of the upper class and their guides late last century became the open domain of far greater numbers with the development of roads,

trains, buses and the private motor car. These gave relatively quick and cheap access to a growing number of home grown tourists who were further spurred on by newly formed mountaineering, tramping, botanical and ornithological clubs. Today National Parks and Reserves have become the playground of many New Zealanders from all walks of life. Increasingly this public has become an aggressive supporter of its National Park system which encompasses approximately 10 percent of the country's total land area with mounting pressure for further extensions to include ecologically important habitats. At the cutting edge of this public voice have been the mountaineering clubs and conservation societies who have initiated the creation of new parks and reserves as well as important additions to existing ones.

High mountains favour a few, but lowlands are accessible to everyone, particularly family groups poorly catered for in our alpine-centred National parks. Okarito Lagoon.
Photo: Bruce Watson

Above left:
The Royal Viking Star off Breaksea Island, Fiordland. The lure of World Heritage status is commonly used to bring tourists to the most special natural sites in the world.
Photo: Craig Potton

Existing lifestyles in the South-West such as fishing, tourism, farming and deer recovery will still continue when the Crown lands of South-West New Zealand become a World Heritage site – an international concept that gives equal emphasis to both cultural traditions and natural heritage.
Photo: D Comer

Far right:
Ski touring beneath the towering Linda Glacier on the slopes of Mt Cook.
Photo: Colin Monteath

Most people enter the South-West on nature's terms and face the same dangers encountered by the early pioneers, foremost of which are flooded rivers.
Photo: Les Molloy

One of the timber viaducts built in Waitutu Forest by the Port Craig sawmill stands as an historic relic of a bygone, exploitative era.
Photo: Geoff Spearpoint

In 1948 the takahe was rediscovered
by deerstalker Dr Geoffrey Orbell high in
the Murchison Mountains of Fiordland.
Today the endangered, flightless bird is
at the centre of a row between
conservationists and deerstalkers.
Introduced wapiti and red deer compete
with the takahe for its favourite tussock
food, and it is important that wapiti and
deer numbers be kept low in order
to ensure the bird's survival.
Conservationists and scientists want to
locate a second wild population of the
takahe, which numbers almost 200, in
the Stuart Mountains of Fiordland, as
a safeguard against disease wiping out
its only wild population in the
Murchison Mountains. In 1986 the
deerstalkers thwarted the plan by
threatening legal action; hopes are high
that this hurdle can be overcome and
that one day trampers might be able to
view this unique rail in its natural
habitat. At present the public is
excluded from the Murchison
Mountains special area
containing takahe.

Photo: Dave Crouchley

Maori and European have responded
with delight and awe to the landscape
of the South-West. Aesthetic and
spiritual inspiration have led to myth
and artistic expression. Although New
Zealand's foremost photographer,
Brian Brake, worked most of his life in
Europe and Asia, he returns repeatedly
to his southern homeland to create
wonderful images which evoke
something of the mystery – even fear –
of this wilderness.

Above:
Mitre Peak, Milford Sound, Fiordland

Right:
Névé, Fox Glacier

Overleaf:
Sunset over Mt Cook

CHAPTER SEVEN

The Politics of Preservation

Maturing as a Nation

Guy Salmon

CONSERVATION first became controversial when it emerged from the mountains to bid for lowland country which might grow grass or timber. The proposed South-West New Zealand World Heritage Area is no exception. The proposal area is dominated by already-protected mountainlands. It is in its lowland parts – particularly in the superb forests of South Westland and Western Southland – that a real conflict has emerged, because the World Heritage proposal invites the rural culture of those regions to look differently on the land, and to adopt a new relationship with nature.

Are these lowlands important? Valley flats of rare kahikatea and splendid red beech, dense terrace forests of rimu, rivermouths of kowhai; the varied scenery of meandering rivers, swamps, estuaries, coasts, these long low forested hills and terraces and rounded granite knobs; the particular animal species which we now know depend on the lowlands: all this is a measure of what we could lose if our conservation commitment here is confined, as in past decades, to the mountainlands.

Primeval expanse

The foremost unique feature of the South-West New Zealand concept is its *wholeness* as a natural creation. The wild mountains here are still skirted by wild lowlands: together they form a vast primeval expanse that speaks its own language and runs its own world. That such a stunning natural asset has survived almost untouched for so long seems a miracle.

Today, the lowlands are in contention. The evidence is that they are largely bereft of mineral wealth, although the dreams of course live on; and their agricultural prospects are negligible. It is the lure of timber that marshalls those of exploitive outlook against the protection of the South-West. Behind their rhetoric about 'the great forest lock-up' lie their own proposals for so-called sustained yield management of timber: proposals which are, in the end, ill-conceived and economically inconsequential.

The biggest problem for the would-be forest managers is the special sensitivity of the ecosystem they want to meddle with. The terrace soils of South Westland and Waitutu carry vast tonnages of standing rimu timber, in forests exhibiting often abundant regeneration, yet this apparent productivity is an illusion created by minuscule growth processes acting through vast periods of time. The soils are among the most infertile in the world. The life-permitting nutrient stock of this finely balanced ecosystem is always vulnerable to crippling losses through leaching caused by the intense rainfall regimes of the region: yet the ecosystem is naturally adapted to prevent this happening. Its growth and cycling of nutrients is extremely slow. The nutrients are conserved by binding most of them up in the trees themselves, and in the fresh surface litter around their feeding roots. The result however is that if all the merchantable timber were removed, there would not be enough nutrients left in the soil to grow another crop.

Far left:
Rimu and crown fern, Rowallan forest, Southland. The Waitutu and Rowallan lowland forests adjoin Fiordland National Park and characteristically have short fat rimu scattered throughout silver beech on rolling marine terraces. This tree was logged in early 1987 to meet subsidised woodchipping and sawlog contracts.
Photo: Gerry McSweeney

The closely spaced trees of the virgin forest form a largely closed canopy, an impressive protection for the whole forest against frost and gale force winds. Natural soil drainage patterns evolved over time are also vital to the success of the ecosystem. If in the region's high rainfall the soils were to support surface ponding for any length of time, the trees' roots would be deprived of oxygen and the trees would die. Altogether, the parameters of this environment are extreme: its infertility, its rainfall, its periodic gales. Yet the sour grey soils and their slow-growing, dense rimu forests have descended through the millenia as inseparable partners, embraced in a timeless dance that moves with infinite slowness to the faintly heard music of some primeval orchestra.

But to the north these ancient and little-understood forests have yielded a bitter harvest to the remorseless thrust of selection logging. Great dying trees lean drunkenly down the logging aisles: gale force winds now whirl through the logging-induced gaps in the canopy and bowl over these exposed, shallow-rooted giants in chaotic abandon. Throughout the "managed" forest is the standing death that comes from ponding: a result of the movement of heavy machinery on soft wet soils. The annual growth rate in these forests is by nature so small that it is easily offset by the mortality induced by logging, to negate the potential for sustained yield. It takes the loss of only one average tree per hectare per year to cancel the annual increment. Such losses have proved almost impossible to prevent once a logging gang and tractor are let loose in the forest. 'The silvicultural niceties of selection management are nearly impossible to attain within the practical realities of the local logging scene,' wrote the Forest Service's own scientist in charge, Ian James.

A series of long-term published studies showed that far from achieving a sustained yield, foresters in South Westland were bringing about a sustained deterioration in the forests. As one logging technique after another was admitted to be a failure, a new one was confidently promoted as the key to success. By 1981, when the foresters had wrecked thousands of hectares of forest with their experimental techniques, their southward march was halted by public protest and the deteriorating remains of their past handiwork in Ianthe and Wanganui forests were given up and committed for clearfelling.

Today, many of the confident foresters who led the sustained yield crusade into the South-West are gone. With the dissolution of the Forest Service they were made redundant, retired, or went back to the simple pine plantations from which they came in the first place. But the forces of confident, can-do industrialism, led this time by the Forestry Corporation, are now gathering for one last determined assault. The forests south of the Cook River, and in Waitutu, are seen by foresters as the last great challenges for indigenous sustained yield management in New Zealand. Yet the credibility of this bid for the forests must surely be assessed on the basis of what has been achieved so far.

There is little real prospect that the Forestry Corporation would achieve a positive sustained yield in these forests. Repeated efforts were made to persuade the Corporation's managers to adopt legally binding covenants over the designated production forests of North Okarito and Saltwater which would have banned heavy machinery from the forest floor, and confined 'management' to the extraction by helicopter of dead and down trees. They refused to accept such a restriction, claiming it would be unnecessarily costly, and an affront to their professionalism. Earlier, the scientist who for years had monitored the logging operations and reported the repeated failures to achieve sustained yield, resigned and was not replaced. There is no way now that the public will really find out what is happening to the Corporation's public forests. With the collapse of monitoring and the insistence on continued use of ground-based machinery, and against the background of the appalling history of forest management in this region, the Corporation simply forfeits the public confidence it would need for any extension of its operations.

While the bulk of the timber south of Westland's Cook River is rimu, there is also a significant amount of virgin kahikatea forest. Because such forest was once extensive on lowland plains throughout New Zealand, and this is the last large area which survives, there are powerful arguments to preserve it. Most of it is swamp forest. The trees'

interlocking root matrix forms a floating platform over several metres depth of dark peaty ooze. Selective logging in this situation – let alone sustained yield management – would certainly be a difficult business, and current experience of it is zero.

In the Western Southland beech forests the sawmillers have teamed up with wood-chippers and the result in current operations is a more-or-less total removal of the virgin standing forest. Although the soils there are less difficult and there has been some success in regenerating the resilient beech, the scenic and recreational impact of logging is severe. The consequences for the region's rich wildlife are particularly bleak: kaka, parakeet and yellowhead, all threatened species, disappear from the forest with logging and have not returned to regenerated stands 25 years later. The logging and wood-chipping contracts expire next year. If their renewal can be prevented, it will be the beginning of a happier future for these forests.

The economics of logging

Economics are – inevitably – a key factor in the debate over the forests of the South-West. The Forest Service's financial accounts have generally shown a multi-million dollar loss on native forest operations in Westland and Southland. By savage pruning of overheads the new Forestry Corporation hopes to turn a profit in the main part of Westland, where clearfelling produces low cost logs, transport distances are short and there is no sustained yield constraint until the mid-1990s when exotic plantation supplies come on stream. But these ingredients for a quick profit just do not exist in the case of a sustained yield timber management project south of the Cook River, nor in Waitutu. If the Forestry Corporation is allocated such areas it will inevitably acquire the Crown's assets for a paltry sum, since the valuation is based on the earning power of the asset.

Even for the most economically favourable areas, the market asset value appears to be less than one dollar per tree, according to studies made by Native Forests Action

Charles Sound, Fiordland.
The establishment of magnificent
Fiordland National Park created no
controversy. It was dominated by steep
mountainlands with little lowland
forest of interest to foresters or farmers.
Photo: Ray Joyce, Lansdowne Press

101

Foresters and the rapacious timber industry have wrecked thousands of hectares of native forests in their failed attempts at management and in subsequent clearfelling operations to clean up the mess. Their legacies are the wastelands they have created in a few decades out of pristine rimu forests such as Wanganui and Ianthe (pictured), just north of the proposed World Heritage area. Now they want to move south.

Photo: Ian Platt, DoC

Council researcher Dr Peter Grant. Many forests have a market value that is close to zero. The risks of failure in the sustained yield enterprise are high, and the low value of the asset provides little economic incentive for the Corporation to prevent its deterioration. The combination of low value and high risk raises a serious question: can it really be worthwhile for the country to commit the forests of the South-West to the Forestry Corporation for production – even if the forest had no special value for anyother purpose?

What of the regional benefits of logging? Assuming no reserves were created, 5.7 million cubic metres of timber would be available south of the Cook River. Cutting through that on a 300-year rotation would in theory produce about 19,000 cubic metres a year. That would keep open one sawmill the size of Whataroa mill, which is currently threatened with closure through reduced wood supplies. There are 33 jobs there. The scale of benefits obtainable from logging the Western Southland forests is similarly small.

In April the National Party announced a policy commitment to legally protect all the publicly owned forests in Westland south of the Cook River. Yet this drew vigorous criticism from National's own West Coast branch, based principally (in the words of their electoral candidate) on 'the continued lock-up of productive lands.' The concern was that 'the West Coast faced the prospect of standing on its own feet on the productive capacity of only 10 percent of the total land.' This oft-repeated claim about the plight of the West Coast needs scrutiny. Most of the West Coast is unproductive mountainland, including the Southern Alps, yet in relation to the needs of the population, there is also plenty of productive lowland. On a per capita basis, the average West Coaster has two and a half times the national average endowment of productive land, outside reserves. The West Coaster also has eight times the national average endowment of potentially productive cleared land lying idle. Land is not in short supply on the Coast: and the land proposed for reserves, even the large area south of the Cook River, actually has a very small and dubious potential for job creation.

Tomorrow could be too late for many trees in Western Southland's Rowallan forest. Haven to kaka, yellowhead and parakeet, these are the most immediately threatened of the World Heritage forests.
Photo: Gerry McSweeney

Tourism's growth potential

The very use of that term 'lock-up' needs to be strongly questioned. The intention of the World Heritage Area proposal is to open up and market the area for recreation and tourism, while at the same time still accommodating to a large degree the established low-impact land uses: moss harvesting, whitebaiting, deer capture, and cattle-ranching in the riverbeds. Of course, the word 'tourism' is regarded by some West Coasters as a code word for putting timber men out of work. Their region is one where thinking about the future is still heavily dominated by traditional primary industries – coal, gold, timber and farming. Tourism is the region's invisible industry, its importance little reflected in the preoccupations of local councils and news media. Yet the reality is that tourism's annual

direct regional benefit to the West Coast measures $96 million: much more than the
timber industry's $61 million. In the controversial area south of the Cook River, tourists
on an average day already outnumber local residents two to one. South Westland's future
is signalled by the pattern in the Franz Josef and Fox Glacier districts, where the tourist
industry's dollar output has grown to four times the combined output of the traditional
industries of farming and sawmilling, and where it is tourism alone that now has the
really substantial growth potential.

Because the natural attractions of South-West New Zealand are absolutely of world
class, measures to effectively protect and promote this area can boost the numbers of
international visitors to New Zealand. For every eight new overseas visitors attracted
here, one new job is created in the economy. All New Zealanders therefore have a strong
interest in protecting our tourism assets and in promoting them through an international
marketing concept, a seal of quality such as the proposed 'South-West New Zealand
World Heritage Area.' A recent exploratory survey of the German tourist market
illustrated the potential from that country alone: 1.8 million Germans are 'very interested'
in making a 3-4 week trip to New Zealand, at a cost of $4,000 or more. Their stated
reasons for wanting to come are overwhelmingly related to unspoilt nature and scenery.
What South-West New Zealand has to offer is precisely what these people are searching
the world for. In an increasingly logged-over, polluted and subdued planet, New Zealand
has retained – so far – a quality of natural assets that powerfully draws people from all

Conservation, recreation and tourism groups have championed protection of the South-West in a far sighted vision to safeguard an international treasure. Conservation campaigners on the South Westland coastline.
Photo: Craig Potton

round the world, and has the ability in future to generate a thousandfold more income for us than could the traditional user of native forest land, the timber industry.

The proposed South-West New Zealand World Heritage Area is a visionary concept that points to values of global significance. The objections to it are of a local character: that a small sawmill might have to reduce production, that the local county might suffer reduced income from logging levies, that nostalgic dreams of further pioneering land clearance might have to be given away. In the ordinary course of New Zealand's provincially-dominated politics, local objections of this sort would normally carry the day, and the attrition of virgin native forest would continue. If there is hope that the global values just might be put first this time, it rests on two possibilities. First, that enough New Zealanders feel strongly about the protection of this area, and will make their view known to the Government. Second, that the local people of the South-West will see for themselves the benefits of the World Heritage Area proposal, and after due consultation, will consent to it.

South-West New Zealand – even its lowland part alone – represents an area so large that its full legal protection would be a major event for the history and culture of our country. Such changes are wrought in the end by committed people whose work brings about a new scale of values in the popular culture. A new, globally-informed awareness of what is valuable; a belief that there is intrinsic value in the wholeness of the natural world; a sense of humility in our relationship to nature; an acknowledgement that there are other values in land than the mere production of physical commodities: these elements are part of the movement for the South-West, and their strength will be tested in the Government's final decision. If the decision is to protect the South-West, it will tell us something new and exciting about ourselves as a nation.

'A vast primeval expanse
that speaks its own language
and runs its own world.'

FURTHER READING

Geology

Maxwell Gage: *Legend in the Rocks – An Outline of New Zealand Geology*
    (Whitcoulls, 1980).
Royal Society of NZ: *The Origin of the Southern Alps* (Bulletin 18, 1979).
G. R. Stevens: *New Zealand Adrift* (Reed, 1980).

Vegetation

Gerry McSweeney: Matai-totara Flood Plain Forest in South Westland
    (NZ Journal of Ecology 5:121-128).
A. F. Mark: Vegetation of Mt Aspiring National Park
    (National Park Scientific Series No 2, 1977).
A. F. Mark and Nancy M. Adams: *New Zealand Alpine Plants* (Reed, 1986).
J. T. Salmon: *The Native Trees of New Zealand* (Reed, 1981).
Kevin Smith: Kahikatea: the Feathers of Tawhaitari *(Forest & Bird* Vol 18, No 2)
Peter Wardle: The Kahikatea Forests of South Westland
    (Proceedings, NZ Ecological Society, 2121: 62-71).
Peter Wardle: Plants and the Landscape in Westland National Park
    (National Park Scientific Series No 3, Lands and Survey 1979).
Hugh Wilson: *Wild Plants of Mt Cook National Park* (Whitcoulls, 1978).

Wildlife

Mike Daniel and Colin Baker: *Mammals of New Zealand* (Collins, 1986).
Graeme Elliott: Mohua (yellowhead), a Declining Species *(Forest & Bird,* Vol 17, No 3).
Carolyn King: *Immigrant Killers* (OUP, 1984).
Jim Mills and Roger Lavers: *Takahe* (McIndoe, 1984).
Colin O'Donnell and Peter Dilks: *Forest Birds of South Westland* (Wildlife Service, 1986).
Readers Digest Complete Book of New Zealand Birds (Readers Digest/Reed Methuen, 1986).

Maori History

Atholl Anderson: *When the Moa Ovens Grew Cold* (Otago Heritage Publications, 1982).
John Boultbee, ed June Starke: *Journal of a Rambler* (OUP, 1986)
Barry Brailsford: *The Tattooed Land* (Reed, 1981); *Greenstone Trails* (Reed, 1984).
Terry Duval, ed: *Te Karanga,* quarterly journal of the
    Canterbury Maori Studies Association.
Ray Hooker: *Archaeology of the South Westland Maori* (Forest Service, 1986).
A Taylor: *Lore and History of South Island Maori* (Bascand).

European History

A. C. Begg and N. C. Begg: *Dusky Bay* (Whitcombe and Tombs, 1966);
    Port Preservation (Whitcombe and Tombs, 1973).
John Hall-Jones: *Early Fiordland* (Reed, 1968).
John and Susanne Hill: *Richard Henry of Resolution Island* (McIndoe, 1987).
P. May: *The West Coast Gold Rushes* (Pegasus Press, 1962).
J. Pascoe: *Mr Explorer Douglas* (Reed, 1957).
Neville Peat: *Cascade on the Run* (Whitcoulls, 1979).
Paul Powell: *Men Aspiring* (Reed, 1967).

Conservation

Forest Service: *South Westland Management Evaluation Programme* (1986).
Joint Campaign on Native Forests: *Waitutu – the Track to Preservation* (1984).
IUCN: *The World's Greatest Natural Areas* (1982);
    National Parks, Conservation and Development:
    The Role of Protected Areas in Sustaining Society (1984).
Nature Conservation Council: *The Red Data Book of New Zealand* (1981).
Resource Management Centre, Lincoln College: *Economic Benefits*
    of Mt Cook National Park (1986).
Roger Wilson: *From Manapouri to Aramoana: the Battle for*
    New Zealand's Environment (Earthworks Press, 1982).

Far left:
Fox Glacier sunset
Photo: Gerry McSweeney

Following pages:
Barrington Falls, Arawata Valley.
Photo: D Comer

A forest creek, George Sound,
Fiordland.
Photo: Craig Potton

'The foremost feature of
the South-West New Zealand concept
is its wholeness .... that such a stunning
natural asset has survived almost untouched
for so long seems a miracle.'

THE AUTHORS

DR GERRY McSWEENEY is the Conservation Director of the Royal Forest and Bird Protection Society. Trained as an ecologist he has spent much of his life working in the South Island's high country tussock grasslands and in West Coast forests and national parks. Though now resident in Wellington with his wife Anne and three children, he previously lived at Franz Josef Glacier where he worked as Westland National Park's environmental interpreter and scientist. Gerry also combines his love of the outdoors and his conservation campaigning with nature tourism trips which he guides to the wild places and national parks of both Australia and New Zealand.

CRAIG POTTON is well known in New Zealand as a photographer and writer on New Zealand's wild places. His interest in conservation goes back to the beech scheme of the early 1970s. He has been involved at a grass-roots level and in local body politics as a Nelson City and Regional Councillor. At one stage he worked for the Native Forests Action Council and he has since been Chairman of Forest and Bird's Nelson branch and is still a member of that committee. Craig is now involved in preparing national park handbooks and photography assignments celebrating New Zealand's wild places. Two books of his have been published in 1987: *Images from a Limestone Landscape* (a book about the new Paparoa National Park) and a book on Tongariro National Park to celebrate its centennial. Craig and his partner Beverley Baseman live in Nelson.

KEVIN SMITH is Forest and Bird's West Coast conservation officer. A childhood in the native timber sawmill towns of the Central North Island developed into a career as a botanist. Active in conservation since the early 1970s, Kevin has lived with his wife, Barbara, at Harihari, South Westland for the last 10 years. As a scientist his special area has been the ecology of kahikatea forests. He has played a central role in fostering conservation interest on the West Coast and in rebutting the often extravagant claims of the timber industry. Kevin has been heartened by the growing awareness in South Westland that forest protection coupled with a sensitive tourist industry provides a far rosier future than exploitive logging.

M. J. COSTELLO

KERI HULME has been active in conservation ever since she arrived at Okarito a decade ago. She was closely involved in the celebrated New Zealand-wide campaign to protect the forests on her doorstep – South Okarito and Waikukupa – which were added to Westland National Park in 1981. Before becoming a fulltime writer and leaping into international prominence with the Booker Prize winning novel *the bone people* she worked as a postie on the West Coast. Keri is a member of the Ngai Tahu tribe with her own family roots in the Moeraki region on the South Island's east coast. She currently chairs the South Westland Mahitahi Tribal Committee.

COLIN O'DONNELL is a wildlife scientist with the Department of Conservation and lives in Christchurch with his wife, Heide, and their two children. He is a member of the Ornithological Society and is an authority on wetland and forest birdlife. His early research work was on the rare crested grebe which has one of its strongholds in the lakes of South Westland. Other research projects Colin has undertaken include wildlife surveys on Lake Ellesmere and the wetlands and rivers of the eastern South Island and a study of kiwis on Stewart Island. On joining the Wildlife Service in 1984, his major project was a comprehensive evaluation of the habits and distribution of forest wildlife in South Westland. A major report on this study has just been published.

GUY SALMON is Director of the Native Forests Action Council. Since the early 1970s his name has been synonomous with conservation. Guy burst onto the scene when he and his wife, Gwenny Davis, led the successful campaign against a massive ill-conceived pulp mill based on North Westland's beech forests. These forest campaigns soon spread throughout New Zealand and gave rise in 1976 to the 341,160 – signature petition, the Maruia Declaration. This was to be the blueprint for subsequent forest conservation successes in places like Pureora, Whirinaki, Okarito and North Westland and also for the creation of the Department of Conservation. Guy and Gwenny live on the edge of Nelson estuary with their son.